Pilate in Caledonia

CALEDONIA

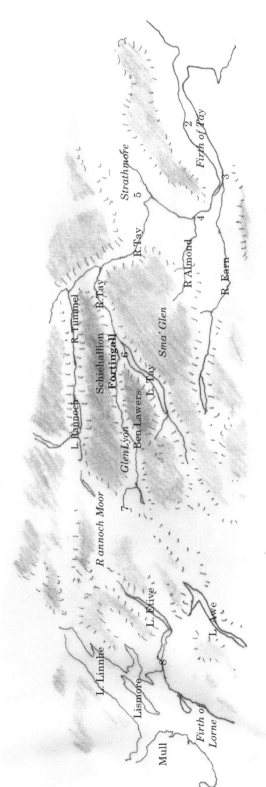

Mull

Lismore

L. Linnhe

Firth of
Lorne

L. Awe

8

L. Etive

R annoch Moor

L. Rannoch

R. Tummel

GlenLyon

Ben Lawers

7

Schiehallion

Fortingall

6

R. Tay

R. Tay

L. Tay

Sma' Glen

Strathmore

5

R. Tay

R Almond

R. Earn

4

3

2

Firth of Tay

1

The Travels of M. Pontius

1. The Bell Rock
2. The Grassy Beach
3. Carpow
4. Bertha

5. Cleaven Dyke
6. Fearnan
7. Tigh nam Bodach
8. Falls of Lora

PILATE IN CALEDONIA

THE CHRONICLE OF THE BIRTH OF PONTIUS PILATE IN FORTINGALL

HISTORIA PONTII PILATI APUD CALEDONES NATI

NEIL HOOPER

SHAUN TYAS
DONINGTON
2012

.

Published by

SHAUN TYAS
1 High Street
DONINGTON
Lincolnshire
PE11 4TA

ISBN
978-1-907730-13-9

title-page illustration shows a
coin issued by Pontius Pilate as Prefect of Judaea

to
Alistair, Ladd, Sheena and Rosie
who first heard this tale

Printed in Great Britain by
the MPG Books Group, Bodmin and King's Lynn

CONTENTS

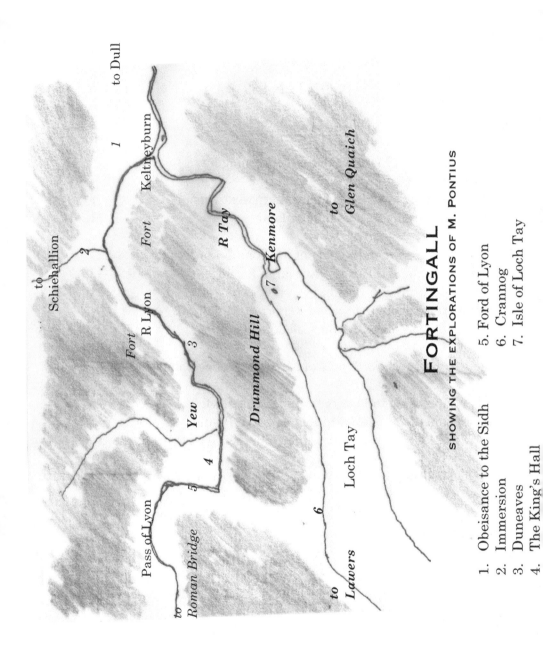

FORTINGALL

SHOWING THE EXPLORATIONS OF M. PONTIUS

1. Obeisance to the Sidh
2. Immersion
3. Duneaves
4. The King's Hall
5. Ford of Lyon
6. Crannog
7. Isle of Loch Tay

to Dull

1

Keltneyburn

to Schiehallion

2

Fort

Fort

R Tay

Kenmore

to Glen Quaich

Fort

R Lyon

3

Drummond Hill

7

Yew

4

5

Pass of Lyon

to Roman Bridge

Loch Tay

6

to Lawers

INTRODUCTION

The tradition that Pontius Pilate was born in the picturesque village of Fortingall in Highland Perthshire is full of inconsistencies and historical impossibilities. When we read in tourist brochures or newspaper articles that Pilate's father was a Roman legionary, when no Roman army came anywhere near Scotland until years after Pilate's death; and when they name Pilate's mother as a Maclaren or a Menzies, clans that were unknown until the late middle ages, we may find the whole idea laughable. Even the less ridiculous version, that the father was an ambassador from Augustus to the leader of the Caledonians seems to lack any evidence or credibility.[1]

I cannot remember when I first heard of the legend of Pontius Pilate's birth in Fortingall, at the mouth of long Glen Lyon; it must have been as a child and long before I came to live at Ardtrasgairt, from where I can look down on the 'bent enclosure' from which it takes its name, in the crook of the River Lyon. This was called 'The Roman Camp' in the days before modern archaeology and historiography. However unlikely the legend was, Scotland did seem to have a strange relationship with the executioner of Jesus Christ – were not the First of Foot, the Royal Scots, nicknamed 'Pontius Pilate's Bodyguard'? Perhaps it all derived from an ironic reaction to the claims that Jesus's 'feet in ancient times, walked upon England's pastures green'. Scottish myths must take the opposing side. When I came to live here after years abroad, where I sometimes was the sole European in far-flung places, I began to feel some affinity with the idea of a lowly legate from the great empire arriving unannounced among the outlandish Caledonians.

I have often been stopped by tourists in the village and asked about the veracity of the legend, or to point out Pilate's birthplace. I tried to find out the truth; but the more I looked the less probable it seemed. It was said to be told in the old chronicles, but none of them have any such tale. It is sometimes claimed to be in the Scottish history of the sixteenth- century English chronicler Raphael Holinshed, the source of other such travesties of history as Shakespeare's *Macbeth*. There is a story in Holinshed, derived from earlier Scottish chroniclers Hector Boece (1527)[2] and John of Fordoun, about the

---

[1]   For a recent reference see Rosanna Cunningham, MSP, in her introduction to Breeze et al., *First Contact – Rome and Northern Britain* (see bibliography).

[2]   Hector Boece, *Scotorum Historiae a prima gentis origine* (Paris, 1527). The author is grateful to Dr Simon Taylor for advice on Boece.

Emperor Augustus sending ambassadors to Metallanus, King of Scotland. But there is no mention of any baby being born to one of them, or indeed any indication that they came anywhere near Fortingall. The chroniclers' invention of 'Metallanus' (or Metellanus) as King of Scotland was anyway unhistorical, as there was no such kingdom until many centuries later. These chroniclers, however, did have a literary purpose in writing about the reign of Metallanus, which was to depict him as a perfect ruler, distinct from the evil rulers who came before and after him. The reason? A good ruler must have been on the Scottish throne at the time of the Saviour's birth.

Another suspect in my mind for the origin of the legend was Gavin Douglas, the great late-medieval Scots poet and classicist, the translator of Vergil's Aeniad into Scots. Douglas was also bishop of Dunkeld, and so the pastoral superior of Fortingall. If anyone had known of – or created – a local legend, it could surely have been him. Moreover, at the end of his life, exiled in England by James V as one of the dangerous Douglas family, he provided material to Holinshed for use in his History of Scotland; but as we have seen, there is no mention there of Pilate. Then again, sixteenth-century Fortingall had its own chronicler, Sir James Macgregor, Dean of Lismore – the early collector of Gaelic poetry. But there is no trace of the legend in his writings. Similarly, after the Reformation, the accounts of the parish by the Fortingall ministers in the *Statistical Account of Scotland* are silent on the matter; they do not even mention the belief to ridicule it.

I sometimes think that the story arose through the kind of misunderstanding that must have been common in eighteenth-century Highland parishes like Fortingall, where the minister and his educated friends would be conversing in English, while the majority of his congregation spoke only Gaelic. Perhaps the minister, showing some guests the ancient yew tree beside his kirk, referred to it having been ancient in the time of the Romans. A bystander, half comprehending, says to his friend "What's the Minister talking about? Romans?" (For a reference to popery would always be suspect) "Aye," says his friend "ye know, like Pontius Pilate". As this conversation gets repeated again and again in different tongues, it eventually changes, as in Chinese whispers, into "The minister says Pontius Pilate was born under the yew tree!"

However, that is just an idle fancy. The first written evidence of the belief comes in some British and American magazine articles at the very end of the nineteenth century. Then there is a letter written to *The Times* by Sir Donald Currie, Fortingall's millionaire shipowning laird and MP, in 1901. Sir Donald, who was mainly responsible for the rebuilding of Fortingall kirk at that time, wrote that among the old stones that had been turned up at the demolition of the old kirk was one inscribed 'PP'. He suggested, tongue in cheek presumably, that even if Pontius Pilate hadn't been born in Fortingall, he may have been buried there. Now Sir Donald was also a friend of notable writers such as Tennyson and Kipling, and it is strange how many supposedly ancient local traditions can be traced back only to his time. Perhaps, I thought, it was all an elaborate joke on his part. I could imagine him lounging at the members' terrace at Westminster, regaling his leader Gladstone with the story of how he had bought this village in Scotland where Pontius Pilate had been born.

And so what follows is only my idea of what might have happened if a lone Roman legate had been despatched by the government of the first Roman emperor, Augustus, a few years before the birth of Christ.

Imagine, then, that my story is a recently-discovered transcription and partial translation from the Latin, of ancient manuscripts purporting to be several reports by Marcus Pontius, later surnamed Pilatus, of his expedition to the Caledonians in c.6 BC, together with an unofficial account not transmitted to Rome at the time; several letters written around 40 AD by an elderly Romanised Caledonian to a correspondent in Galatia, giving his account of the same expedition; and official comment on the reports.

From the condition of the papers, the language used and the handwriting, the documents would have been copied sometime in the mid nineteenth century from a somewhat earlier document. Either the original translator or the copyist must have been Scots, as some Scots expressions occur in the English sections.

It might be, of course, that all these papers were the creation of one of the local literati, compiled in the tradition of Macpherson or Chatterton. If, however, these documents were based on genuine originals they must have been found and put together by someone with access to manuscripts, or transcriptions of manuscripts, dating to around the first century AD. Pontius's report and the comments thereon, could, we may imagine, have been transcribed into one of the many compilations that eventually found their way into the Vatican archives. The letters to the Galatian – who appears to have been an early Christian – could have been preserved and copied in an Anatolian monastery, perhaps transferred to Constantinople in the face of the Muslim advance, and thence to Rome after the fall of the former city. How all these came to Scotland must surely have been because of the Grand Tour. Whether a Scottish scholar – perhaps a Jacobite – had the time and inclination in Rome to search the archives for documents relating to his homeland; or maybe an Italian go-between, amassing antiquities relevant to the tourists of the different nationalities he dealt with, put them together and sold them to one of the many Scots that came his way. Sometime later they may have been passed on to someone with the knowledge and interest to transcribe and translate them – a minister or schoolmaster perhaps whose work remained obscure and unfinished.

While I might have attempted a full and scholarly edition of these fictive documents, I have merely put into a readable form enough of them to make a coherent, and I hope, interesting narrative. I have added some notes to make some more obscure references comprehensible, and to point out connections to the history and antiquities of the region.

I present The Chronicle of the Birth of Pontius Pilate in Fortingall.

Neil Hooper
Ardtrasgairt
2012

THE FIRST REPORT OF MARCUS PONTIUS CONCERNING HIS MISSION TO CALEDONIA

I. SALUTATION

In the name of the Commander in Chief Caesar Augustus to the prefect of the north Publius Maximus, legate to the General Staff, territorial consolidation division, from Marcus Pontius, specialist field officer, Caledonian intelligence project, greetings: herewith the executive summary of the obligatory quarterly project reports covering the field action years of the project AUC 748–750.[1] These reports have been compiled quarterly in accordance with para II subsection XXXV(a) and are submitted at the end of the project as allowed for under exception IIIB of subsection XXXV(c).

II. INTRODUCTION

In accordance with the project action plan agreed with the Division on the Ides of November AUC 746, I embarked at the northern port of Gaul on the Kalends of April[2] AUC 748 in imperial galley no LIV under the command of Titus Trebobius, legate with imperial commission for an exploratory circumnavigation of the isles of the northern sea, commonly called the Britannic Isles. For details of his voyage please refer to his report. As far as concerns this project, I need only mention that I was provided with, as a guide, the slave Lossio and that on the tenth day of sailing north and north west, having kept the coast to port, we came to a gulf, triangular in shape and of equilateral dimension around 20 miles. This was reported to be the estuary of the Bodotria river, and sometimes referred to as the Caledonian Sea, as the tribes living north of that sea are generally reputed to be part of, or allied to, the Caledonian nation, while those to the south are more closely allied or related to the British tribes of the rest of the island. The point where the shore curves round to the west to form the southern shore of this sea is marked by a conical hill on the coastal plain, and a massive and precipitous rock about a mile out to sea, home to a multitude of large and noisy sea birds. Heading north a flat island is passed at about mid channel before nearing the extremity of the northern shore. From here the land, known as Fifa in the tongue of the place, seems fair enough for the twenty miles until the estuary of another great river, the Tavus, where I was to make landfall, flows into the Germanic Sea.[3]

---

[1]   i.e. about 6BC to 5BC.
[2]   i.e. on April 1st.
[3]   Bodotria: the Forth; Tavus: the Tay. The flat island was presumably the Isle of May; Berwick Law and the Bass Rock can also be identified.

III. ARRIVAL

The preliminary project plan envisaged a landfall on the Tavus as this would facilitate the journey into the heartland of the Caledonians, and the suitability of the district for further landings and logistics could be assessed. The entrance to the estuary is about one mile wide and protected by many shallows and sandbanks; access at low tide is perilous even for small craft should the captain be ignorant of the channels, and virtually impossible with large galleys. At high tide access is easy and good shelter and anchorages are available as the estuary widens immediately to a good two miles from shore to shore. After about three miles of sailing upstream, the land parts on either side, forming a veritable inland sea, but much of it is too shallow for navigation at low tide. The south side is lined with gentle hills; on the north, before a range of greater heights, the shallows merge with marshes and a plain abounding in game and wildfowl.

Ten miles sailing to the west, the estuary narrows to a distance of three hundred paces; an island and great banks of rushes hide the channels. After waiting for high tide, and proceeding under oar and taking soundings, we arrived safely at the confluence of a river flowing from the south west; here is a good anchorage, with deep water where a port could be built; a strand where boats and even galleys could be beached; firm and defensible ground and easy communications by land and river; for the Tavus is navigable for five further miles by boat or a galley of moderate size and paths lead along the smaller river, called Erenus, into the heart of the territory of the Vacomagi. To this place provision could be brought by sea for an army advancing from the south. Indeed its importance is recognised by the local tribes (the Venicones) who have established nearby a primitive fortification which they call Dynpol.[4] Here also soldiers and supplies can easily be taken across the Tavus by raft or by floating bridge; while that river itself leads to the mountain strongholds as well as the granaries and forests of the Caledonians. The natives have, however, also constructed a sort of acropolis, a fortification of massive boulders around the summit of a hill dominating this region. Any plans for the use of this place as a base would have to take account of this.

Here on the 10th day before the Kalends of May I disembarked with the newly freed Lossio, who as translator and guide under contract, negotiated for a boat to take me as far as the river is navigable. This having been arranged, the legate Titus prepared his galley, now reprovisioned with water, meat and grain obtained from the natives, for departure. The omens being propitious,

---

[4]   Carpow, near Newburgh, Fife. The Roman fort built later has been identified with Ptolomy's Horrea Classis – the "granary of the fleet". A log boat similar to that described was recently found buried in the mud near the mouth of the Earn.

my last night of civilisation was spent on the galley, which was to sail on the tide at one hour after sunrise.

As for me, my embarkation was at dawn into a primitive vessel approximately five paces long but less than one pace across, constructed by shaping roughly the trunk of a massive tree to form between the beak and a square stern a hollow hull with no seats: I requested that a bench might be inserted for me, but this was refused – indeed the practice of squatting low inside the hollow both provided some shelter from the chill wind and, more importantly, stability to the primitive craft, which could only make the journey upstream with the flow of the tide to help it. It carried us past rocky heights which could command entry to the region, up to the tidal limit, a place called Bertha where the river swings northwards, dividing into a number of torrents and marshes to form large flat islands which the natives use for their tribal assemblies; these could be useful for army training and for sports. Here the river can be forded, and even, if civilisation came to a region so remote, bridged. It would be awkward for permanent settlement, but a good defensible site lies two miles upstream at the confluence with the Tavus of a stream called Aman.[5]

IV. PROPOSED ACTION

From the natives idling on these islands at Bertha, I engaged two bearers for the overland journey. Questioning of the more articulate of the natives confirmed the chief camp of the current Caledonian strong man to be some forty miles distant – the slave Lossio, it transpired, was from a northern tribe, and had only travelled to the centre of the nation from other directions. To reach this place, we would have to follow the river Tavus almost to where it issues from a great lake in the mountains, and penetrate to a strongly defended valley near the mountain which these people hold sacred.

Document Committed for Transmission to Titus Trebobius, Maritime Legate

---

[5] Now the Almond. The name Bertha, given to the fort Agricola built here, is sometimes held to be a medieval back-formation from the Pictish name *Perth* (a copse – Watson, p. 356); if the text here is genuine it might indicate that Bertha was in fact the name the Romans used.

My First Landing in Caledonia: An Alternative Version
(For My Friends' Eyes Only)

Yet I did not record here my first landing in Caledonia – that episode seemed to me to detract from the formal brevity of my report, to which as a novice in official reporting from barbarian lands I was strictly adhering – though in the later stages of my narrative I admit to straying far from these confines. Perhaps at that early stage I did not wish to record or even recall the terror I felt or call into question the actions of our sailors, although I should have paid due gratitude to the gods for our deliverance.

Our progress north from the Bodotria estuary was hampered by the increasing velocity of the winds and their inconstant direction. By the time we reached the Tavus the storm was such that not only the passengers but most of the sailors were incapacitated through sickness and fear. As the wind had now turned to blow from the north-west, it seemed impossible to enter the estuary, and we were driven out to sea past its entrance. We might have maintained this course had we not come upon a fearsome omen, some horrid feature of the deep was causing the waves to break upon it so that the sea seemed to boil in front of us.[6] With tremendous efforts and the direction of all fit sailors and our own slaves to the oars, the master managed to bring the ship around and steer south-west back to the Tavus. But right across the entrance to the estuary a line of breakers was pounding the shallows, and there seemed to be no way through, till we saw a small native boat rise out of the waves before us and speed through a narrow channel between the breakers. We redoubled our efforts in an attempt to follow its course and prayed fervently to the gods, until, the wind miraculously veering behind us, our ship seemed to leap across the waves then speed more gently through calmer waters. We passed close to a headland to the north, where a primitive wooden structure seemed to house some native look-outs, and headed for a sheltered beach about a mile to the west. Here we anchored, and when the captain had ascertained that the ground was suitable, he decided to pull the ship up at the height of the tide to check the soundness of the hull.

First we had to give thanks to the gods for our deliverance, and check that any natives nearby posed no danger. The captain gave me the honour of being first to set foot in Caledonia; I was to go unarmed with my slave, to show that we presented no threat, while our shipmates, with their arms ready but concealed, watched from the ship. Lossio and I waded up a sloping shore,

---

6   This must have been the Inchcape or Bell Rock, later made famous by Southey's poem and Stevenson's lighthouse.

7   This sounds like the 'Grassy Beach' at the Stannergate between Broughty Ferry (where there has long been a castle guarding the entrance to the Tay) and Dundee.

where mud at the low watermark turned to small sharp stones and above them a pleasant grassy bank.[7] The surrounding land was mainly flat, but immediately before us a pine-clad hill terminated in a cliff which afforded some shelter. We had brought with us some small tokens of friendship for the natives, and a flagon of wine for a libation to the gods. I had poured just a sufficient offering to the gods and spirits of the place, when I saw two natives approaching from the east. They stopped at a distance and raised their spears. I held out my hands to show I was unarmed while Lossio tried to establish communication. Then I realised that they were not the only natives present. The spot had seemed to be unpopulated, but now a horde of children appeared from their hiding places behind bushes, even from clumps of grass or it seemed out of nothing at all (indeed the rough dwellings of these people often merge into the ground itself so they are indistinguishable to the stranger). The fears of these children having been set at rest by the presence of their guardians, they came up to us and chattered around us, the more forward of them feeling our clothes, shoes, and even hair. I looked to see what I could give them, and came upon some fruit we had taken aboard in Iberia – the captain had a superstition that his sailors should squeeze some of the fruit into their mouths every day as a nostrum against gumrot. Having no knife to cut them into pieces, I opened one roughly and handed it to the children, who eagerly bit into the outer parts and found them bitter. Not being disposed to waste their gifts, however, they took all I could give them and made off towards a small settlement I now made out only from the smoke of its fires rising to the westward. The native guards, meanwhile, had accepted a ration of the wine and were happy to sit on the grass and talk to Lossio, while our crew, having observed all that had happened, prepared to land and beach the ship. We thus spent our first day and night in Caledonia pleasantly enough, as the storm subsided and we discovered this spot to be blessed by Apollo. It lies, as I later ascertained, about three miles east of a fortified settlement and harbour, which though insignificant to a Roman eye, is considered major in these parts; to face southwards in these Boreal regions is advantage enough.

Before we left, the children brought us a small pot containing a strange sweetmeat; then Lossio explained to me a custom of the women of the place, that when they have fruit that is too bitter to eat they boil it with water and honey so as to let nothing go to waste. The result of their experiment with the fruit was palatable, but not something that would tempt the palate of the civilised world.[8]

---

[8] The invention of Dundee marmalade is generally credited to James Keillor in the eighteenth century. Perhaps he was inspired by a folk memory of this incident. The fruit here is, however, unlikely to be oranges which were unknown in the Roman world, but may have been citrons, which were used medicinally at that time.

THE STORY ACCORDING TO LOSSIO,
THE FIRST LETTER

To my former brother in servitude, Mennius the Galatian, from Lossio the Caledonian, greeting: in our former letters we have recounted our histories and that of our world and recalled our old words and thoughts in the academy of the slave cells; when we first struggled with the tongues of our captors and compared our own, discovering that we two, from opposite ends of the world, were yet of the same people.[9] We dreamed then of freedom, for ourselves from slavery and for the world from the yoke of Rome; yet now, when peace should soothe my age, I see them prepare for war against my people. But it is not the plots of Claudius that I have to write about, for your news of the man or god you call the Prince of Peace has amazed me: these are indeed glad tidings if they be but true – as we once talked of the mountains and rivers of our homes and the spirits of the streams and the trees and asked why these were not enough for men and why the gods of war and power should bring us slavery and generals and tyrants – yet what I have to tell you is of a small part I played in this drama. For you write that this god-man from Nazareth suffered under Pontius Pilate the procurator of Judea – can this be the same Pontius whose birth I saw among my own people more than forty years ago? I have told you tales of that foolish master of mine who came among the Caledonians, think-ing to bring them with fair words and a sprinkling of Latin under the power of Augustus; how my lord was himself made captive by his desire to lie with the daughter of our king, and how in the end it fell to be my task to carry the resultant squalling infant back to Rome – did I not say that my master's sur-name was Pilate? Did you know when you wrote to me of the passion of your lord that there would have been no power to crucify him had I not saved this wretched babe from ignominy or death?

There was no sign that Pontius would have a role in the stories of gods and men when I saw him first at Bononia,[10] gazing at the grey-green seas of the sleeve of Albion – unless it was a gleam of terror in his eyes at what he saw as a voyage into the unknown, which to me was to be a homecoming. I could still sense that fear through the feigned self-importance with which he greeted the captain when we boarded ship; and it became real enough when we hit a north- easterly gale off Ocelli Head. It needs no soothsayer to explain Pilate's fear of water – enough of it came aboard that night! And the fuss we had when

---

[9]   The Galatians (to whom St Paul addressed one of his epistles) were the most easterly of the Celtic nations in classical times. They settled in the region around Ankara, now the capital of Turkey.

[10]   Boulogne.

we left the ship at Dynpol on the Tay and he had to sit in the bottom of the boat to go upstream. He would insist on having a plank across the top to sit on in state, but he soon realised it was safer down below! He sat huddled down, his face as green as if we were in a high-sea storm, his arms stretched out aloft to grip the sides of the boat, seeing nothing – later he had to ask me for details of the river and country to include in his report. Our boatmen gazed in wonder at this man of the race of Rome, conquerors of the world, sunk to a sickly heap. I tried to encourage him by extolling the scene, describing the cliffs as towering above the river, as fine a sight as any in Italy. He did not look up, yet I heard that he boasted back in Rome that he had that day discovered a new Tiber. So did he bend the petty truth to his own benefit and his country's renown![11]

---

[11] There is still a tradition in Perth that the first Roman there exclaimed "Ecce Tiber!" – "Behold the Tiber!"

EXTRACTS FROM THE SECOND REPORT OF M. PONTIUS CONCERNING HIS JOURNEY ALONG THE TAY

Editor's note: *The report covering the next part of the journey is rather patchy and inconsistant. It may be that the Roman was having difficulty in coping with the discomforts of travelling in what seemed to him a wilderness. He was at home neither in the log-boats that conveyed him up river where navigation was possible, nor on the rough tracks that had to be traversed where the river was too shallow or swift. He gives little detail of what, if anything, he observed, even finding it difficult to orientate himself where "the mists and clouds are such that the sun at noon can only vaguely be discerned, and finding the pole star at night is virtually impossible". He did notice some kind of crowd assembled on a low hill near the east bank some way north of Perth; while it is tempting to identify this with the moot hill at Scone, and thus establish an early importance for this site, the description does not have enough detail to make identification certain. It is not until he approaches the junction of the Tay with the Isla at Kinclaven that his report begins to have some interest.*

At the point where a fair stream enters on the right-hand side as we go against the current, the Tavus begins to curve round to the left towards distant mountains. The tributary seemed to flow along a wide vale,[12] with signs of cultivation and pasture, which is surely the source of some wealth for the Caledonians, and it is to be wondered at that their chiefs reside not there but among the hills. At such a parting of the ways a fortification could well be established that would dominate the wealth and strongholds of that nation.

There was now a diversion from our river route; first we clambered once more into a boat which this time ferried us across the Tavus a little way past the confluence. Then we struck away from the shore for several miles over rough country, but well wooded, until we came to a wide glade in the forest. Turning to the west, for on our left side the afternoon sun had at last appeared and shone low on our faces, we began to walk slowly and silently along what at first seemed to be a wide road, almost as if our legions had reached there many years ago, and this was the remains of their engineering. However, as we progressed, this 'road' became more of an embankment, with ditches and low ramparts alongside, and gradually rising higher. I noticed that each of my companions had, as we entered the glade, picked up a handful of stones and earth: this they carefully preserved as we went along. Finally, this low ramp we were processing along culminated in a sizeable mound, which we stood round for

---

[12]   This must be Strathmore.

a time silently; then each of my companions in turn deposited their handfulls of earth and stones on the summit of the mound, before turning to the east, then the west, and breaking their silence with wild yells, ran down the sides and off into the forest. My guide, Lossio, urged me to follow them. I feared that we would be lost among the high trees and dense undergrowth, but setting ourselves resolutely towards the setting sun we eventually came upon them making camp in more open ground on the slope of a pleasant ridge from which the river could be seen winding its way from some distant crags.

Puzzled by the strange ceremony we had taken part in, I tried to extract its meaning, but no one could explain it clearly; it was, they said, something they always had to do. After much discussion between them and Lossio it was suggested that the final mound was the burial place of an unknown hero from an age long forgotten; in ancient times their rough forefathers had over many years built the processional way to its summit. By preserving a ceremony whose purpose was unknown, they not only honoured the ghosts of their ancestors but propitiated the spirits of that place.[13]

Next morning we walked away from the morning sun towards these rough cliffs, and found the river flowing through wooded hills, the land on the far side full of well-grown timber, on the near, pasturage for the many cattle that are the wealth of these people. On a low hill near the river stood a primitive acropolis, which I learnt served as a strongpoint for the Caledonians who hope thus to dominate the lesser tribes of the region. As we neared, guards armed with spears accosted us; after discussion with my companions, however, they showed us every consideration, providing us with a convenient craft hauled upstream by a party of warriors on the bank for several miles until the river was again too shallow for the craft to proceed, and we had to resume our progress on foot. Our baggage ponies, which had on other occasions provided the motive power for our boats going against the current, were now ahead of us, and we did not catch up with them until we met another, faster, river entering from the north,[14] while the the main stream bent round again to the west. Here I had the advantage of being borne across the new stream by the pony, while, the weather being fine, the natives splashed across with juvenile screams and cries.

[13]   This ceremony must have been held at the Cleaven Dyke, the neolithic *cursus* at Meiklour. It runs more in a north-westerly direction, so it may have been late in the afternoon. The carrying of stones and earth to the summit may be a recollection of the way the *cursus* was built: it is suggested that it was lengthened periodically over many generations, extending its use as part of the ceremony. The Romans did build a temporary fort, as suggested, at the junction of the Isla and the Tay, but their great fortress was not built there but at Inchtuthil, probably near where the party camped that night.

[14]   The Tummel.

A few miles further on we camped for the night where the Tavus suddenly pours his waters down furiously over half-hidden rocks, so that for at least one hundred paces the black surface becomes white foam broken only by jagged points of stone.[15] While we were resting, a native in a simple craft of basketwork and hide sped across the pool below the rapids to offer us travellers trinkets to barter. I was amazed to see among these trifles a finely wrought brooch of finest gold. I learnt from Lossio's enquiry that specks of gold can be found in some of the streams coming down from the hills; with great perseverance enough can be gathered to be worked, and even among those primitive people good craftsmanship is found.

The path was now at the foot of craggy hills separated from the north bank of the Tavus by flat marshland, the more impenetrable for the myriad of bushes and small trees growing there.[16] On the slopes of the hills, between the path and the crags, limited pastures lay interspersed with attempts at cultivation. The guide indicated that a gloomy grove on a hillside we were approaching had some superstitious significance for this place, which he called the Dale; but this did not prepare me for the ecstasy the natives in the party were to exhibit when, on rounding a ridge and attaining sight of the next valley, they dropped to the ground and lay prostrate, their arms stretched out before them.

After some minutes of what appeared to be supplication to the dirt beneath their lips, they raised their eyes slowly to gaze into the distance. For myself, I could see only sky ahead, between the slopes at the head of the valley; until slowly the mist seemed to dissolve and the gaunt shape of a high peak appeared in the distance as if in the heavens. After such an exhibition I was not surprised to learn that this peak was the holy mountain or Olympus of the Caledonians, to whose gods supplication and propition was due.[17] Yet what appeared to be a barbarous ritual was also a practical necessity, for there was a fortification on the brow of a hill which faced us to the south and stretched away to the west. This fort guarded the entrance to the Caledonian capital; and to the sentinels there any visitor not performing the ritual indignity branded himself an alien, an enemy or a traitor.[18]

In my time with the Caledonians, to keep the trust I had laboured to earn, when travelling by this route I had to comply with the ritual. I did not, however,

[15] The rapids at Grantully are now much favoured by canoists.

[16] Probably the carse of Dull, where later St Adamnan founded a monastery.

[17] Schiehallion is usually said to mean 'the Fairy Mount of the Caledonians' (Watson, p. 21), although Macara derives its name from its resemblance to a maiden's breast. From the south it has the shape of a giant neolithic burial mound, the 'sidhe' of Gaelic folklore, where the ancient gods or fairies lived.

[18] The remains of a fort (Dun Mac Tuathail) on a western brow of Drummond Hill can still be visited.

compromise the dignity of Rome: to prevent contamination I first spread my cloak upon the ground, and lowered myself only on one knee; and could justify the stretching of the arms towards the mountain by the inevitable presence of the Divine Julius amongst whomever of the other gods resided there.

The lie of the land beneath the hillfort was now apparent: the river had branched in two below it; behind the hill to the south, so I was told, the Tavus flowed out of what was strangely termed 'the water city'; its tributary, winding round the hill before us and leading us to the capital (if such a simple settlement can be so-called) was named the Lugodon and sacred to Lug, the same divinity that is worshipped in Gaul.[19]

We had not gone far along this 'holy' river to the west and away from the 'holy' mountain when I experienced something of the ferocity of what passes there for religion. We had come to a mountain torrent, but instead of looking for a place to ford or leap across we halted beside a deep pool where the black water swirled as if by the fury of its natural demon. My companions drew aside, and I started with amazement as I beheld, converging on me, two savage giants, naked but for the matted red hair that covered their filthy bodies, and with their skin tattooed with strange and devilish patterns. Before I could compose myself, they seized me one to each shoulder and dived with me between them into the raging pool.

Pressed down deep in the water, in breathless terror I could only assume that this was either their way of disposing of unwelcome strangers, or of sacrificing to their river-god; but I had just made a vow to Neptune to dedicate my next year's salary to him if I survived, when I found myself lifted up into the air and onto the further bank where I lay panting in agony. I was not left there long, but was raised as if from the dead by my fellow travellers who had crossed this barbarous Lethe by a more convenient route,[20] and I realised that my immersion was some kind of savage initiation; that having survived it I was in their primitive eyes an accredited ambassador; for my wet clothes were stripped from me and I was wrapped in a multicoloured heavy woollen cloth; this was belted around my waist and draped over my shoulders like an outlandish toga and, clothed as a pilgrim to a primitive shrine, I was led by a band of natives, of the same stature and appearance as my submersers, but clothed and armed, to where a war chariot of Gaulish design was standing. Two of my escort pushed me aboard this contrivance that seemed designed more for show than for speed or efficacy on the battlefield, drawn as it was by two small black horses over rough ground, alternately muddy and rocky – the science of road making having stopped many hundreds of miles to the south.

[19] The River Lyon, is here associated with the French city, but Watson (p. 453) points out that the Dean of Lismore spells it 'leivein', probably meaning 'grinder'.
[20] The stream would be the Keltney Burn.

After about a mile of this jolting we stopped on a height above the river, opposite to a large circular hut which stood a little distance from the other shore. This edifice, simple as it was, appeared to be of some importance in the neighbourhood;[21] and there appeared from it in a small procession a strange figure; as he approached I could make him out to be an aged long-bearded man, bent and crippled, who as he painfully gained the riverbank, let out a piercing yell and was lifted bodily up by two attendants – much as I had been, but instead of being immersed he was carried dry across the river. As he drew near, I was pulled from the chariot and pushed down to kneel before him – indeed in that posture his aged eyes were level with mine; and his eyes stared hard into mine for a full two minutes, as if by some divination he could comprehend a certain mystery therein. Then his eyes closed tight as if he had concluded that that mystery was unutterably tragic; and I looked around for my interpreter to assure him – for he must have been some influential counsellor or priest – that I was the bearer of goodwill from my great lord, indeed of good news about the future of civilisation in which his people could share; but Lossio whispered to me that this was a holy man and prophet to be revered in silence, and that I should save my speeches for the 'king'; the old man sank down as if in prayer to an invisible spirit, and I was led back to the chariot, and on through lines of warriors, clutching spears and great swords so long that two hands would be needed to wield them, while up on the hill, in the trees and above the crags, came the glint of more arms.

It was good, sir, that I came alone on a peaceful mission; for if I had come with force a whole legion would have been needed to penetrate this fastness; and I admit my fault in pressing you for an armed escort. Notwithstanding, however, being forced to submit to indignity, I was otherwise unharmed.

More ritual had to be endured before I could meet the leader that they called a 'king'. We soon came to a ditch and wall of earth – not regular as in our camps, but following the line of the ground, as if abetting nature, not in control of it; and I was made to remove my shoes and carry them, although, even if the ground was holy, it was certainly rough underfoot. The object of this veneration was soon apparent – a gigantic tree of yew, with a trunk of such girth that it could well have been (as the people claimed) a thousand years old.[22] Beneath this tree sat a family of stunted idols: stones that had been worn by the currents of the river into shapes roughly indicative of a man and his family.[23] I was given to understand that a libation to these gods of the tree was

---

[21] Duneaves, on the south bank of the Lyon at this point, gets its name from the Gaelic *Tigh-niamh,* the house of a *nemeton,* or sacred spirit.

[22] The Fortingall yew is now estimated to be 5,000 years old.

[23] Such stones are still respected in Fortingall – supporting the meaning of 'Lyon' as 'grinder' (see note 19).

called for. Some of the people brought forward small wooden bowls of milk, poured out a little of the milk before each of the stones but not before the largest – this father of the stones was left for me to honour in the same way.

These formalities having been completed, I asked to be taken to the leader. I was advised, through Lossio, that he knew of my arrival and that I would presently be taken to him. Meanwhile I should take my ease. Ease, however, was not an appropriate word for my situation. I was left in a dark and miserable hut, with a fire in the centre that produced more smoke than heat and light. Rough wooden planks at the side held a pile of a withered but tough fernlike plant; covered with animal skins, this served as a couch. Nor were any delicacies forthcoming to welcome me, but after some time a bowl of milk was proffered me together with a coarse cake of some ill-ground and ill-tasting grain; this was plucked before my eyes off a flat stone in the fire – I knew not how much of the ill-taste was of ashes or the nature of the grain. My hosts departed, taking Lossio with them; I had to endure a long wait alone, and had just managed to make bearable the discomfort of my couch and close my eyes when I was pulled upright to face a barbarous individual whose half naked body was disfigured by crude markings or tattoos. He glared at me with bloodshot eyes: I did not demean myself by holding his gaze, but examined his strange skin symbols. Serpents there were and fantastic beasts, but some that seemed to be signs of Venus or Vesta rather than Mars: not swords or spears or shields but a mirror and a comb. I was about to tell Lossio, who had reappeared, to give him my greetings, if he was a chief or king, or if he was a herald to take me to the king, when the painted personage burst into a tirade in his tongue, chanting in a higher and higher tone for what seemed almost an hour. At last, with a shout, he stretched his hands above him and ceased; then Lossio spoke briefly in their tongue, and as I heard something like my name and that of Rome, I guessed he was presenting me; but there was no opportunity for further diplomacy as the ensymboled one turned and strode out. The others followed, leaving me in a solitude which lasted at least till morning.

I passed the time sleepless until shortly before dawn I was woken again by an urchin bearing a steaming bowl and a jug of milk; the bowl contained a concoction of the consistency of thick mud and apparently made of the same grain I had been given before. I found it unpalatable, but managed a few mouthfuls washed down by as much milk as was in the jug. My need for ablution was now pressing: I found the urchin with a guard at the door and mimed washing my hands. With an impudent grin he led me to a stream and I had to make a more basic mime to let him understand my more fundamental prime necessity. With an unseemly hoot he took me to a foul smelling little hut above a slight hollow, with a roughly hewn plank above a stinking pit the only convenience. These necessities having been completed, I was brought back to find that at last Lossio had made his appearance.

I reprimanded him for leaving me alone and in such primitive conditions, and for witholding information. The excuse he offered was that he had been working on my behalf to convince the natives that I came honourably and in peace and to make possible my introduction to the leader. He explained that it was no easy matter for a stranger to meet the leaders of the Caledonians, unless brought before them as a captive; and that false tales had reached even to this valley of some alleged perfidy of our Republic and a supposed desire on our part to conquer the world. It was not just their policy to humble strangers by making them wait, but there was a genuine need for some counsellors to be persuaded that I should not be better put immediately to death. I remarked that doubtless one of these ill-disposed was the fierce painted man of yesterday; but no, he was as I had guessed before, a kind of herald or seneschal, and his speech was not a tirade against me, but a lengthy rehearsal of the lineage of the rulers of the Caledonians tracing their descent, if you can believe it, from the gods of the mountain. I asked if this is what the signs on the man's skin depicted, and to which goddesses pertained the mirror and the comb; the answer showed the barbarians in a new light, for I was told that they represented the lineage of the female line; the leader's right to rule did not come down from his father, but from his mother, or perchance from marrying the queen; and although these matriarchs would cede to their men the title of king and leadership in war, in policy the women held the power. Thus I would have to wait not just until the chief was persuaded to see me – and if his priests adjudged the omens aright – but only when his ladies had given their permission.[24]

Thus it was that I stayed three days in this confinement, my only air and excercise the walk to the stinking hut and the stream, my only company – apart from Lossio's occasional consultations – the grinning urchin and the guard. This man I judged of evil aspect. He had a fierce scar across his left cheek and when he entered the hut on the second night just as I was preparing for what rest I could get, I thought I was to be knifed in my bed. However, he only curled up close to the fire and went straight to sleep. It was not until later that I learnt of his hospitality: this was his home, and he had sent his family away – all but the grinning urchin – to accommodate me, and only the chill night damp had driven him to presume on my solitude.

On the morning of the third day, Lossio arrived with some attendants, better clad than those I had seen before. I was mightily relieved to see that they were carrying my packs which I had not seen since my first arrival in the valley – more than the recovery of my personal possessions, I rejoiced that I had the

---

24   Whether or not this is an accurate description of Caledonian polity, the matrilineal succession of Pictish kings (categorically described by Bede) has long been a matter of dispute, as is the significance of combs and mirrors among the more masculine Pictish symbols. It is sometimes asserted that Macbeth's claim to the throne rested on his marriage to Gruach. Elsewhere, similar matrilineal succession has been observed in societies such as the Maldives (see Ibn Batuta: Travels).

gifts that could be presented to the King and, if need be, the queens. Lossio informed me that now I could prepare to meet the chiefs. I was able to dress myself as becomes a Roman, choose a length of rich fabric and a good sword as my first gifts, and pick out some coins bearing the image of Augustus as well as one of the Divine Julius. We walked for half a mile through small fields, some of grain and some of pasture, and then through a wooden gate in massive earthen ramparts. Inside this primitive fortress various huts were spread at random, not in order as we do; and the defences only curved round half the camp, the other side being bounded by the river. In the centre a squarish mound had been raised, and an oblong wooden building of a fair size. Its wide doors were open, but well guarded; I was motioned to wait, until my painted friend, the herald, appeared, intoned some more incomprehensible mouthings, then led us in. Inside, the hall was dark after the daylight, but lit somewhat by two flaming torches at one end and a fire in the middle. Above the fire, between the torches, on a rough bench (the only seating in the hall), sat a tall man in a saffron cloak to whom Lossio made obeisance. I also inclined myself, as much as accorded with my dignity, and offered my salutations.

As Lossio translated my greeting and the Caledonian responded, I could make out in the gloom two women standing at the back on a large flagstone – the floor otherwise was of earth, baked to something like clay around the fire. Behind them the tatooed herald grasped a huge spear which seemed to be set into the stone – I learnt later that these were the symbols of Lug, the god or hero of the river that looped round the enclosure: the stone he had cast across the river to establish the site of his capital, while the natives believed that whoever bore his spear into battle would never be vanquished. One of the women was a veritable hag, the other tall and comely enough: priestesses or queens as I surmised.

Then Lossio spoke the leader's words: "The stranger from the sunland is welcome with us. We will hear his news of the far lands and their ferlies: tell us of the deeds of his kings and commanders, of their great halls and strongholds, their wise men and their champions, gilded chariots and silver stallions, golden girls and gracious queens. He comes alone, so in peace: but as a friend or to threaten war?"

Then I spoke: "I come from our prince and commander Caesar Augustus in the name of the senate and the people of Rome. His laws and protection now run in all lands around the great sea of the south, even up to the furthest shores of Gaul. Tyrants and lawbreakers tremble at his power but his friends outside the empire prosper, as do the citizens within it. Here is his head on these silver pieces: take these as tokens of our friendship. And here is the head of his divine father Julius, who came to Britain in our fathers' time to hold the hand of friendship to the kings and nations of this island. From Rome I have carried this sword and this cloth: accept them as gifts to seal our friendship. To tell of the glories and greatness of Rome needs much time. Admit me to your presence throughout the weeks to come, and I will reveal the secrets of our civilisation, our great city and her colonies, our legions and their invincible arms, our navies and the wealth of our trade. These are not just travellers' tales: I can demonstrate to you the wealth of the empire and how to share in its bounty."

Through Lossio he listened, glanced round at the queens, and then answered: "We are grateful for your gifts and will hear your words: live with us here and leave a true friend. But friendship must be free: we have heard of this Julius who came from Rome with weapons hidden in the hand of friendship, bringing demons to destroy those who spurned his smiles. And with all his pomp and power he was chased by our southern warriors back to Rome, where he fell, so it's told, with his chest pierced by the daggers of his friends. What are you offering, stranger, true friendship or Roman friendship?"

"Both Caesars have been true friends to true friends," I replied. "False friends and traitors suffer the punishment they deserve. The might of Augustus punished the murderers of Julius and established peace through all the empire. He does not need to seek new conquests; good men anywhere will work with us. Only those who work against us need fear his vengeance."

Perhaps Lossio's version of these last words produced a stronger effect than intended: the queens looked at the herald who lifted the sacred spear from its fixing and took an aggressive step forward. The king lifted his hand, it may have been against me or to hold back his men, and I added quickly: "My Lord, I come alone; our nearest armies are a year's march from here, how could I not come humbly to seek peace and friendship?"

"A year's march!" he cried. "All the might of Rome would take fifty years to fight its way to here, and once here all your clanking legions would be slaughtered like cattle and the holy river would run red with their blood. But you, my lonely Roman, you are our guest. We are not Romans to sell you into slavery..." (here he gestured towards Lossio). "Stay and tell your tales of wonder to our warband and our maidens; and perhaps you'll see some wise ways in our life beyond your kenning, go back home with something more than e'er you dreamt of!"

At this instant I was surrounded by a jostling band of youth; their spears, brandished or carelessly swung, persuaded me to go with them with no discussion. They took me a fair distance, to a ring of stones. I was pushed to the centre, while each of the youths sat down with his spear on the ground pointing towards me and his back to a stone – there were in fact nine stones, and each was shared by three youths. They started shouting at me, but whether their words were insults, greetings or questions I could not tell, until Lossio arrived with an older youth who took up his position on a flat stone inside the circle. It transpired that the shouts had been a combination of all these – questions indeed, but which could be taken as either amiable or insulting, as they mostly seemed to concern my family or my virility. However, now that their leader had arrived, their questions became more sober and I was able to satisfy them on many matters concerning our armies and methods of warfare. This band of young warriors was, I learnt, an innovation. Caledonian warriors had traditionally gloried in individual feats of battle, wielding their huge swords from cumbersome chariots. This new band of lightly-armed infantry is perhaps their primitive attempt to combine the flexibility of our auxiliaries with the discipline of our legions.

THE STORY ACCORDING TO LOSSIO, THE SECOND LETTER

From my last letter some impression must have been gained of the character of Pontius the father; but what of my countrywoman, his mother? If your Nazarene was the son of an omnipotent god or a god himself, why did the fates choose a Caledonian to bear his earthly executioner? And my small part in this affair – was I blindly picked for this minor role, or marked from my birth as ill-omened, or blessed as but an insignificant cog in a great yet mysterious machine of salvation?

You should know this custom of my people when an important stranger comes among them: as a sign of friendship and hospitality, to keep him content and at peace, and to preserve the chastity of the generality of our maidens – a girl of the appropriate status is given to him in a marriage that may last only the duration of his visit.[25] Whether such courtesy should be extended to the Roman was hotly debated during the days after his arrival, and if a wife was to be given him, whose daughter it should be. Nobody, of course would give him one of the queen's daughters – that would have been too close to the succession. The king had daughters by other women, but that still would be too much of an honour for a Roman to be given. Most were in favour of drawing lots among the daughters of the charioteers when a solution to the problem presented itself. The king's mother, who had charge of the young girls of the family, dragged before the assembly a maiden who was struggling and screaming abuse at her elders. Her dress and body paint seemed to be those of the common girls who follow the fighters, yet she was fair and strongly built, and could have a noble bearing when not squirming and yelling like a drab.

He can take this one, the queen said. She wants a man, but who of our people would have her? She insults us with the care we have given her, she thinks only of herself, yet everything she does only harms herself. The Romans think they can conquer the world – let this Roman subdue her!

The girl's voice rose up in a whine both childish and termagant, complaining at being fed to this soft and pompous Roman, led like an ewe before

---

[25] A similar custom was observed by Ibn Batuta in the Maldives.

a ram. She would not prostitute herself before this weird wanderer: she'd find her own man and mock at them all.

There was silence – for a girl to utter thus in the presence of the queens and the chief!

Then the king spoke: "Daughter, this is my decree and the decision of the queens. You must thole it, whether it brings you joy or suffering, delight, desire or despair. Your duty is to sate the stranger's passions, to find through his heart the secrets of his mind, and then tell to us the true purpose of his coming here, the hidden thoughts behind his words. Your mother was the priestess of our sacred grove: her curse and our judgement will be upon you if you fail."

At the mention of her mother the girl screamed that they had killed her to make the sun shine and the rain rain, and they now get milk and drink while she lies cold beneath the tree. She would rather have been killed herself than be offered up as a sacrifice to play her lust in perfidy, to prick the might of Rome, a pretty spy for policy.

I have reconstructed her speech out of our tongue as best I may after all these years, to give you an idea of the fierce native rhetoric that is typical of the more vociferous of our females: Princess Nemet was an earthy and expert 'flyter'.

The king held up his hand to stop the tirade, and gestured to the seneschal, who held the girl while the ladies forced a potion between her lips which shortly sent her into a quiet yet sensuous daze. They laid her on a couch of furs in the midst of the assembly, where they rubbed her skin with sweet oils and dressed her in a fine robe, circling her wrists and ankles with delicate torcs of gold.

I was instructed to bring the Roman from his quarters. I found him bored and irritable, but his eyes gleamed when he heard that a girl was to be given him for his pleasure and solace, and that she was fair and comely – I did not tell him of her wild tongue. When I said that she was a daughter of the king, his eyes widened and his chest rose, but his eyes narrowed again when he heard that her mother had been a priestess who had been killed to save her people from famine (yes O Mennius your Jesus is not the first to die to save his people. It was her bent body that marked her as holy, to serve the spirit of the place, and then to be a sacrifice to the fates).

But I warned him: she is not a plaything, a barbarian harlot to be cast aside at will; you must treat her as you would a Roman wife (though I doubted that to be a virtuous model) and only divorce with honour when you depart. It is your honour they wish to test, your sincerity and your virility. If you think you may falter at this trial you can still refuse the lady graciously.

This advice was not well received – what could I, a barbarian too, tell of such things, to a man from Rome, the capital of intrigue!

FURTHER EXTRACTS FROM THE
SECOND REPORT OF M. PONTIUS

For two days I was free to walk around the camp, and once was able to accompany several of the young warriors to a look-out point on the heights behind. This was a singular mark of trust towards me, as I was able to make out the whole disposition of the fortifications and the approaches from all directions. Apart from the valley along which I first had come, this stronghold was well protected. The heights where I now stood were steep and well wooded; to my right a narrow defile wound westward into mountains of horrendous aspect; to my front the river, having emerged from the defile, ran south straight along one side of the camp before turning sharply eastwards along the base of another hill. Just before this bend a path led to a ford and a track climbing up a ridge between the hills due south; over this ridge from a sufficient height could just be perceived a stretch of water among the hills, so that the destiny of the southward flow of the river seemed to have been to reach and flow out into a lake, but some mighty force of nature had wrenched it from its way and turned its course away from too quickly finishing its labours.

On enquiry I was informed that, as I had guessed, this lake was the so-called 'water-city' and the source of the Tavus river; my companions were to be going to its shores the next day, and promised to take me with them.

The same day I received a further honour from the chiefs of the Caledonians. One of the customs of this nation is to provide a superior form of hospitality to those visitors worthy of respect in the shape of a maiden of high degree to serve as his concubine: it is in their eyes a kind of marriage that lasts only as long as the visitor's stay among them. The virgin I was to be so honoured with was a princess: no less than the daughter of the king by a priestess of the sacred grove. I was summoned to the great hall where the princess was waiting for me, arrayed richly – according to their standards – and reclining on a couch of furs, surrounded by all the chiefs, queens and warriors of the nation. It seemed that their rite did not allow for any kind of interaction between us, however, as the princess gave no sign or response when I greeted her; but lay as if entranced even when four warriors lifted her up and bore her to my hut.

You will not wish, oh imperial legate, to hear the intimate details of my relations with the princess, which did, however, make me privy to deep secrets of the Caledonians and unrivalled understanding of the barbarian mind; suffice it to say that when she roused herself from that ritual trance it seemed that our marriage would be one of form rather than substance, and that the honour granted me would indeed add to my dignity, but at some cost to my domestic peace, rest and repose.

The next day, when the young companions of the war band came to take me to the lakeside, my princess concealed herself from them among the furs of our bed, giving no acknowledgement of their greeting or of my words to her; but once I had started off with the warriors she appeared behind us, and followed us on our excursion, just close enough to be considered by an onlooker to be attached to our group, yet never in fact being part of it.

The path climbed straight for a mile to the top of the ridge, from where we could see the lake down below us – we seemed at the apex of an angle, one arm going east behind a headland called, I was told, the nose of the alders;[26] the other stretching south-west into the distance, terminating in two small far off peaks. The south-facing slope was fairly cultivated, with here and there large round huts with rough stone walls and pointed reed-thatched roofs. As we came down nearer the shore, I realised why they called this place a water city. A lake-dwelling had been erected some paces from the shore, built on a platform held up by massive timber posts, the hut somewhat larger than those in the fields, but with wattle rather than stone walls. Such structures I had seen in the Helvetican lakes, and they seem to be constructed not so much for convenience or for defence as to display the standing of the chief of the locality. Looking up and down the lake, I could now see such structures every one or two miles – the whole lake is around twenty miles in length and two across – each big enough to house a family of twenty or more. Boats of various sizes, but similar to the one I had boarded after leaving the galley, were being paddled with surprising alacrity between these waterhouses and various points on the shore, so it was easy to imagine the lake as a kind of city with a water network of streets.

As we stood some paces from the shore, watching the traffic on the lake, my princess slipped past us down to the water where a large boat was approaching. As it swung round at the beach she stepped lightly through the ripples and up and onto it, sitting high at the stern as the craft glided away, the sun breaking through the clouds lit up her golden hair, the boat black against the silver sheen of the water.

I tried to find out what this might portend, but I was hustled down towards the nearest lakehouse, where my companions had business to transact. Inside, this water residence was as dark, smokey and insalubrious as its landward equivalents. Not having Lossio to effect proper introductions or formalities, I was of uncertain status, being simultaneously ignored and the object of furtive curiosity. After an hour of dreary incomprehension, the

---

[26] Fearnan on Loch Tay is named from the Gaelic for alders, which were used in the construction of the numerous lake dwellings or crannogs on the loch. One of the most notable is the Oakbank crannog at Fearnan, which has been intensively excavated by the Scottish Trust for Underwater Archaeology.

muttered consultations between my companions and their hosts drew to some sort of conclusion. As we proceeded to the shore I gestured to the boats moored there and tried to ascertain where my princess had gone and if we could follow her. My efforts seemed to arouse some laughter and sympathy, and after much lively discussion two of our party took me into one of the craft, and we set off towards the east end of the lake. Having experienced this form of transport early in my expedition, I was now more accustomed to its insecurities and was able to take note of my surroundings. The hills along the lakeside were somewhat precipitous and tree clad, except where clearings for some simple agriculture had been made in the vicinity of the lake dwellings; rough shelters could be seen around these clearings, but whether for animals or for the humbler workers on the land I could not be sure.

As we proceeded, a cold wind arose in our faces which made our progress less comfortable, but eventually I made out a dwelling in the lake larger than the others, so large that it might well have been on a natural rather than a man-made island.[27] It stood at about one hundred paces from where the lake seemed to end, a beach curving over to the right, and but a narrow expanse of water between that and this island revealed the outflow of the Tavus river. I was not granted a view of the interior of this island 'palace', however, for as we came into the primitive harbour that had been constructed there, my princess appeared, running wildly along the stony quay, and with a cry that seemed to be of both joy and derision, leapt into the boat, yea into my arms, making the poor craft sway perilously, my heart struck with both joy and fear. I held my wife tightly, as one might hold an untamed cat or puppy, dizzy with delight, suspicion and the sickening motion of the boat. The Caledonians treated this display with mirth, seeing no danger where the water was only a few feet deep, and shouting greetings, farewells or taunts (I could not be sure which) to a tall, comely youth who had appeared on the quay, applied themselves to their paddles and a fair voyage home.

Having approached the heartland of the Caledonians from the south and east, I was eager, both from my own curiosity and in fulfilment of our project plan, to explore the access to and from the western shores of this land. I was told, and could myself see, that the way westward was all but barred by horrid mountains, whose slopes were clothed in mist and drenched with rain even more than the settlement where I had been for the most part confined. These mountains were in effect the boundary of the Caledonian territory, their leaders being more concerned to exploit the fertile lands to the east than stretch a species of control across the barren lands to their few kinsmen of the west; be-

---

27   Later known as Priory Island, or the 'isle of women', the Isle of Loch Tay was where King Alexander II established a nunnery in memory of his Queen Sybella, who is said to be buried there. It later became a Campbell stronghold.

sides, the aboriginals of that coast were slowly being supplanted by settlers from Hibernia; up to now the Caledonians have regarded these Scotti with tolerance, keeping the western Caledonians well occupied behind the mountain barrier, but some of the younger counsellors wondered, as did I, if on a longer view they might have been better to fear a new power in the west that might break out into the east.[28]

There are two ways to the west from here: the broad way starts from the west end of the city lake, the journey thus commencing by boat would be by permission of the people of the lake; so that although the way from then on is quite broad and easy, my companions preferred the narrow road for their more privy excursions. To reach this road the defile with its raging torrent to the west of the camp[29] has to be by-passed – the main path goes up through the woods behind the camp, but I was taken first across the ford and west along the south bank of the river; with my princess and my companions I made slow progress for several miles across rough and sloping ground, through many bogs and streams until we came to a larger torrent, cascading wildly down a high precipice into the river. This stream, being easy enough for a light band to cross but somewhat of an obstacle for a fully equipped legion, led us to a discussion on tactics and logistics, into which I introduced the topic of bridge building, of which the natives are strangely ignorant. Any defile that cannot by crossed by simple planks defeats them. I explained the theory of how a stone bridge may be built out of small stones cunningly placed to support each other as an arch; as I could not overcome their scepticism, I promised to demonstrate such a construction at this spot after our return. I thought of this as a thanksgiving for our safe journey; I did consider the appropriateness of teaching the natives a process that could conceivably be of military significance; but decided that any such danger was minimal and outweighed by the developmental and diplomatic advantages of such a project.[30]

In any case, my companions had tired of my instruction and sought diversion in pursuing the game which they said abounded on the slopes above us. They bounded off up a precipitous and narrow valley above the waterfall, while my princess and I, who had become more intimate as we journeyed together, followed behind. The stream descended this valley by leaps and pools; at one of these which seemed imbued with a mysterious energy I was reminded of an ode of Horace that had struck even my unpoetic ears before I left Rome: the scene was so auspicious that I attempted to mould what I recollected of his

[28] The settlement of Argyll by the Scots from Ireland is usually dated several centuries later. The earlier contacts indicated here are, however, not surprising.

[29] The Pass of Lyon.

[30] This appears to be where the so-called Roman Bridge in Glenlyon was built: but this is more likely a Victorian folly than a genuine Roman construction.

verses on the Bandusian spring to this wild water, and vowed a sacrifice there
that would seal the bond between my princess and myself:

O sweet pool in the mountain stream
Darker than ebony, you deserve
This garland of flowers which I lay
On your still surface.
Now you draw them down
With the white torrent
From the rocks above;
Tomorrow I will give you a lamb
Whose first horns are beginning to bud
Destined never to curl:
Its blood will redden your waters
Where my girl will clasp my hands
Sanctified

Our companions having reappeared with a fine hind shot for dinner, we
crossed the stream and ran down the hillside to a ford across the river, whose
valley had broadened out into a wide pasture backed by a fertile terrace. From
here the path westward was fair going for ten miles, the mountains standing
back to allow sunlight and level marching, with good supply of timber on the
lower slopes and fertile settlements at regular intervals. Then the hills came in
closer beside the river as we followed it up towards its source; the land around
was wild and had the appearance of frontier country: the few men we saw
came out to accost us from small circular stone constructions they dignified
with the name of castles.[31] In one of these, larger than most but ruinous and
unroofed, we camped for the night and roasted our deer, the inhabited build-
ings being too primitive to afford our band hospitality – besides the new war
band prided itself on its self-sufficiency, in contrast to the usual reliance on
hospitality or rapine for sustenance.

Next morning we toiled upwards to where the river issued from a deep
lake confined by steeply sloping mountains, along whose side we had to pick
our way. After a mile of rough going we turned right along a small arm of the
lake, then followed a little valley towards a ridge high on the western horizon.
My companions encouraged me with extravagant claims that the western ocean
was but a few miles off – and I ascertained that the saddle ahead did indeed
mark the boundary of the main territory of the Caledonians. Perhaps because
of this, the valley held some spiritual significance for them: the hill looking
down on us from behind was, they said, possessed by some guardian spirits,

[31]   There is a line of small ring forts in Glen Lyon reputedly associated with the
       Fingalians; one of these is at Cashlie.

while the valley itself, whose waters provided the source of their holy river, seemed to embody their earth goddess – they called it the old woman, and I was about to meet the old man. The princess had broken away from my hand and bounded past the companions, heading for what appeared to be a small heap of stones. As we drew near I discovered it to be a primitive temple in miniature. The stones were roughly formed into a little house, sheltering a curious petrine family – related no doubt to the idols I had been introduced to under the ancient yew tree at my first arrival. The largest of this tiny family was the old man – he was ceremoniously removed from the shelter by the priestess my wife, followed by the smaller stones, doubtless the old woman and their family. They had remained in the shelter for the winter, and had to be moved into the light again for the summer. By this ritual the priests pretended to ensure good weather in the summer and warm houses for the winter; whether the old man was also the god of the river at whose source he stood, and thus Lug himself, renowned throughout Gaul, I could not ascertain.[32]

This ceremony did at least give us spirit to ascend the final ridge; where I mocked my companions saying 'Where is the western ocean, then?' as nothing appeared before us but more hills, streams and woods; but they only laughed and leapt down the westward slope with wild whoops and yells. And indeed, after I descended from the heights I myself felt strangely invigorated, almost at home. The wind did blow a fine rain into my face yet the air felt as though from somewhere much further south. I was told that the natives called the rain that always drenches these shores the tears of their ocean god, who loves this, his northland, so much he keeps it from the snow and ice that should assail it. Be that as it may, I was to find out later that day of the strange relationship between the land and the sea. The journey from the mountain foot, across a river dangerous to ford, and for ten miles along a wildly wooded valley, had become tedious, so we were overjoyed to spy ahead, blue in the rare evening sunshine, a peaceful lake. The men ran ahead to set up their camp, my princess pulled me by the hand, we ran to the shore, she dipped her hands in the water and splashing cried 'Taste it, taste'. I scooped up a handfull, drank – then spat out the brine: this was sea water, and not a lake but an arm of the ocean: for all along this coast the sea blends with the land, twisting around for miles in among the mountains. The flow and ebb of the tides are not limited to the open sea, but find a home among islands and hills as though the land is part of the sea's domain.[33]

* * *

32   *Tigh nam Bodach* (the house of the old man) is in Glen Calliche (the old woman's glen), and is where this pagan ritual is still carried out.
33   A similar description is found in Tacitus' *Agricola*. As Tacitus had never visited Scotland, he perhaps took his description from Pontius' report. However, Pontius' description is itself suspect: the 'wooded valley' seems to be Glen Orchy, but this

THE SECOND REPORT OF MARCUS PONTIUS

After the equinox had passed, the days became short and the nights longer, and the Caledonians prepared to move to their winter quarters. Their cattle which had been roaming the hills, guarded from predators – human and animal – by relays of the warriors, were brought down to the valley and division made among the people, for some were to stay there for the winter and some would accompany the leaders to their lowland camp. I, being desirous of seeing more of the country, and having established good relations with the young warriors, was permitted to go with them as a vanguard to make sure there were no enemies waiting for them. Our route would be somewhat of a diversionary tactic, albeit by a more direct way, over a steeper pass than the main body would use. The cattle were also allotted, the smallest portion accompanying us, the next remaining in the valley, the most going with the chiefs. Our group first had to ford the river, and go over the ridge to the lake. While some of us boarded a fleet of boats, the others herded the cattle round the shore. The boats met the herd at the outflow of the Tavus, and guarded them as they were swum across. We then camped on a gentle sandy beach at the head of the lake, before heading up the hill to the south. This was a hard climb, but took us to a desolate plateau, then down to a steep valley, well sheltered with a goodly lake at its foot. The natives called it in their tongue 'the drinking vessel'.[34] The weather being fine, the morale of the men was high. One of them, called by me Votianus in an approximation of his name in Latin letters, had a joyful voice and sang continuously: some short lyrics in which others joined, some were long and repetitive, as if the nation's history was being retold in barbarous epic form. Some seemed to be directed at me and I guessed them to be somewhat obscene, referring to my separation from the Princess, who was travelling with the queens. This merriment concealed the dangerous purpose of our journey, because as we descended into the lowlands we might meet hostility from those of the local tribes who resisted the power of the Caledonians. We were to winter on the south-facing slopes of the valley of the Erenus, at the mouth of which river I had disembarked so long before. The Vacomagi, who had previously dominated this region, still held the land to the south of the river as their own; those who remained to the north either peacefully accepted Caledonian rule, or did so only superficially, nurturing discontent within their hearts, silently seeking an opportunity to harm their oppressors.

So it was that while we drove the cattle out of the high valley, over rough terrain, then descended steeply into another narrow valley, dominated by close heights on both sides, the stream running through it, I learned, being the upper

leads to the head of freshwater Loch Awe, and several more miles would have to be travelled to reach the sea lochs Etive or Fyne.
[34]   Glen Quaich.

waters of the Amun which reaches the Tavus at Bertha, a band of these discontents were watching us. They must have taken up positions hidden behind boulders high above the narrow valley, but Votianus and his friends were either unaware of the danger or were too proud to show their care, and mingled their songs with the bellowing of the cattle, until a shower of stones and arrows fell upon us. The cattle panicked, and charged forward, followed by most of our fellows. The bolder of the warriors clambered up the hillsides, yelling terrible cries, and put the attackers to flight, powerfully and accurately flinging their spears. When I judged it prudent to come from behind the tree which had given me shelter, I discovered that just one of the Caledonians was lying slain on the path. An arrow had struck down Votianus in the midst of a song. He was buried by his companions beside a large rock[35] in the midst of the valley, then we sadly hastened to catch up with the fleeing cattle and the rest of the band.

This was a loss felt grievously by the whole nation, as his music was to have played a principal part in a great feast that was to mark the onset of winter, and the establishment of the Caledonian capital in the south ... *[several pages of the manuscripts at this point are decayed and practically illegible; they appear to be mainly a complaint about the hardships the writer suffered throughout the long dark northern winter].*

On the ides of March, my princess, being big with child, was ordered to be carried on a litter back to the northern camp, where she would be taken into confinement by the women of the tribe. I spoke not about the significance of the date, but as winter was still hard upon us, expressed my sorrow at being deprived of the warmth of her body and of the pleasure of presiding over the birth of our child. But both the customs of the tribe and her own birth to a priestess prevailed against me. It was with difficulty that I was allowed to accompany her bearers and their guards on the journey. Nor was I pleased to see that she was accompanied all the way and even to the birthing house not just by the crones whose duty it was to assist at such events, but by Pencaw, the leader of the war band. I would have forced myself into his place, but Lossio pulled me back, saying that his attendance was an honour to me as well as to her; and I followed at a dignified distance to salute my princess and her entourage as they disappeared from ordinary view. Then followed days of anxious waiting.

Pencaw – it was apparently his duty – brought me news of my princess's health, while I mused on the harshness of this place where winter obliterated spring, last year's miserable bounty gone and no sign of warmth or growth. I did, however, realise that I was waking in the morning to be able to see the rain, the floods, the snow or the frost, not just feel in the dark the calamities

[35]   A rather suspect tradition locates Ossian's grave in the Sma' Glen.

of the weather. The animals, meanwhile, must have had a premonition of spring as I discovered the first weak lambs had been born to the ewes that shared with their shepherds the warmth of their huts.

It was on the day I calculated to have been the equinox that I was at last informed that the birth of my child was imminent; this seemed to be well-omened, in a place where in winter the days are so dark that but a slight distinction from the night can be perceived, yet in summer the nights are bright, the sun not seeming to set but to dip down and merely cast a shadow across the surface of the earth. There the progress of the year is marked not as with us by the growth or decrease of the sun's warmth, but by the lengthening or shortening of the days. So it came about that as the day had drawn level with the night and looked fair to win the laurel, I heard three cries from the hut where my princess was confined: the first of unbearable pain that made me shudder; the second mingled several voices in triumph and relief; the third the first cry of an infant. I ran to enter the hut, but was prevented by Pencaw on guard; immediately the head of a crone emerged from the door covering and waggling, mouthed at my opponent. He turned, clapped me round the shoulders as if in congratulation, and made a sign with his fingers that I trusted to mean that at last to me a son had been born.

Being now the father of a fine boy I turned my mind to his future, whether as a Caledonian or a Roman. I must admit that when I accepted my princess from my hosts I did not foresee the consequences of procreation. On the one hand the babe was my son and should be accorded the privileges of a citizen of Rome; on the other his mother was a barbarian and his coming into the world had been marked by savage rather than civilised procedures. How could I ensure that his upbringing would be suitable for a Roman, except by extracting him from this wilderness and hastening him to the protection of our Empire? Or should I abandon him here to grow up a primitive Caledonian outside the bounds of civilisation, yet perhaps to be a great warrior, even a king among them? Could I even contemplate staying to watch over him, never see my home again but live with my princess and guide my son to local greatness? What might an admixture of Roman blood achieve among these primitives? The great Julius had a son by the Egyptian queen, so such fatherhood cannot be dishonourable, yet there was little glory in the life of Caeserion, and then how that woman did ensnare Antonius into degeneration, treachery and ignominious death! Nobility in Rome comes from our ancestors, but now Augustus does not favour only the pure-bred Roman, but oft places his trust in those born outwith Italy and whose blood is strengthened as bronze is, two metals blending to produce a stronger. Such thoughts troubled my mind even as I put on a mask of delight at my fatherhood.

Having none of our augurs to consult, I cast around for omens, but my troubled mind could divine nothing definite from what might have been signs around me. The flights of birds, the winds, clouds and heavens have a different aspect here from home. It needs a native seer to interpret these, and unschooled though they are, they have insights denied to most of us. Their greatest prophet was the ancient hermit who had greeted me so strangely when I first arrived, and as my princess was of his blood I might first have gone to him. Yet I was kept from him by tales of his infirmity or an obstinacy in refusing to countenance my approach, whether from bodily weakness or hatred of outsiders I know not. I had heard tell, however, of a local sybil or wise woman who dwelt on the slopes of a high and desolate mountain which rises above the lake a few miles to the west of where the path from our camp comes down to the shore. I resolved to put my trust in her, and to visit her secretly.[36]

One night when I was with my companions at a feast in the king's hall, and all the men of the guard had grown sleepy with drink, I stole out of the camp, and the moon being full and my familiarity with the land now sufficient to my purpose, I reached the vicinity of the sybil's dwelling by the middle of the night. But to find the exact location was a problem, until I became aware of a scarcely perceptible fluttering across the face of the moon, which led me to pray to Diana for assistance in my quest. Instantly the fluttering creature became more distinct, as not one but three bats which came down to circle a javelin's length away around my head. As I raised my eyes to them they began to move off up the hillside, guiding me, I hoped, to their mistress. The way was rough, and I stumbled often and found the climb arduous, my head swimming with weariness and the circling of the bats, till I tripped over some root or stone and fell into blackness. I struggled to get on my knees and saw before me an ancient hag sitting beside a fire that burned with strange colours as she fed it with I know not what. I attempted to address her in what I had learned of the language of the people, but she laid her finger on her withered lips and seemed to speak, although what might have been a beard or wild hair obscured her face. I know not if it was a dream or if she had a gift of tongues but I understood her as if she was speaking in Latin, that is I made out her words but their meaning still escapes me:

> To face the face of the son, impotent in power,
> The doom of the almighty, darkness to light:
> the undying to death, life beyond life,
> Judge of the righteous.

I made nothing of this jumble of words, except that the final salutation seemed to promise a noble career for my son. Yet could I trust such juggling with

[36] This seems to be on the southern slopes of Ben Lawers, an area long associated with prophecy, a much later example being the seventeenth-century 'Lady of Lawers'.

words? Desperate to hear more, I rose up and stumbled towards the fire. The shadow of the hag seemed to grow and extinguish it. I fell forward again and when I could lift my head from the mire I could see nothing but the moon going behind a cloud and the desolate hillside disappearing into the darkness. I realised then that I was lying on an outcrop of rock covered in primitive carving, mainly of simple hollows surrounded by circular grooves, a pattern which had an important yet undiscovered relevance for the natives.

I know not how I returned to the camp. Wild and fantastic images oppressed my mind as I fell exhausted upon the wool and bracken bedding in my primitive quarters. Tired though I still was, I woke early in the morning chill, my memory full, not only of the savage mysteries of the night before, but of what I was deprived by this vain exile from civilisation. I got no joy from recalling happier times, when I would awake to the care of a domestic slave, stroll down a paved way to the baths, go on to the theatre or the stadium, where battles and dramas are below us in the arena or on the stage enacted by gladiators and slaves, where we are spectators and not forced to be protagonists ourselves. My body ached for the warm room at the baths, to be cleansed in comfort, then refreshed with cooling waters; here one can only stagger shivering into an icy torrent, mocked by the natives for whom a layer of grime is regarded as extra clothing and protection from the cold.

As I lay there my thoughts were interrupted by three or four of the young guard bursting into my hut laughing, they pulled me from my bed and thrust a rough horn beaker before my face, urging me to taste. Great and small fears beset me – was this poison from an enemy or a rival in love, or merely some disgusting potion or brew they had discovered to have narcotic or inebriating effect? I assayed the liquid with my nose, to be assailed with a divine sense of home, for in truth it seemed to be wine, old, rough and unwatered, but certainly wine. I took a moderate draught, and passed the beaker to my friends who hastened me out and away to a place near the great yew where a few goods are sometimes offered for sale by passing pedlars. There a fellow of crafty aspect stood holding a small wooden cask out of which he was dispensing rations of wine to an ever increasing circle of natives. I found Lossio standing somewhat aloof from the crowd and asked him where this nectar had come from. The wine merchant, hearing my Latin, greeted me in a foul version of our tongue. From his garbled words and Lossio's interpretation I gathered that he had come from the west where boats sometimes reached from trading posts in the south of Britain. There they exchange furs, metals and slaves with traders from Spain for our southern wine. Thus our water of life reaches the furthest places of our earth.

Copy of report committed to V. Bibonius, mercator, for transmission to Rome.

EXTRACTS FROM THE THIRD REPORT OF M. PONTIUS CONCERNING HIS GREAT ESCAPE

I know not if it was the unaccustomed unwatered wine, or the sight of the young warriors laughing in their cups, those same young bloods who had been guarding my family's hut, and seemed to have a free admittance there which was denied to me, the husband and father: but a fire of rage and jealousy rushed to my head, and I strode through their rabble to the door of the hut. Inside I stopped while my eyes accustomed themselves to the gloom. I saw first three guards, excluded from the celebrations and with long swords held out at arm's length, points to the ground, standing round the central fire facing outwards. As I moved past, I made out a couch at the far end where lay my princess; at a stool by her feet crouched one of her women, rocking the babe in her arms. I approached to admire my son, when my princess half raised herself towards me with such a strange light in her eyes, of welcome, hope, despair, fear, hate, love, I could not tell but it so inflamed my soul that I flung myself to her and took her in my embrace, tasting the salt of her tears on her cheeks. But comfort her I could not: the guards leapt from their places and two of them pulled me away while the other held back my wife. In fury I yelled out in both tongues that I would have my rights as husband and father, but the two warriors gripping my arms and pressing their swords to my back, forced me to the door. Outside, a strange silence oppressed the gathered crowd.

Nobody made a move until Lossio appeared, held out his hand to mine, and led me from my captors. We walked in silence through the camp down to where the river bends round, by a great pool; there the water seems still but underneath swirls and eddies as if in unseen torment. I knelt down and dipped my face in the stream to wash away the passion in my brain, then turned to my freedman and enquired what barbarous custom it was to tear a husband from his wife and child.

Lossio seemed first unable to answer, but then began slowly: "It is no ordinary woman that bore your child. You know her wild spirit, how she seemed untamable, yet submitted to your love to bear your son; remember her birth, from kings and priests, her mother the chosen one who died to succour the eternal tree of life. Our wise men tell how her child by you will have an awful, incomprehensible destiny; having borne that child, her fate is to succeed her mother as the supplicant of the nation to the life force of the earth, the air and the water. Your part, in fathering the child, is over."

I stayed silent, gazing at the stream. What could I say when such horrors are spoken so calmly? But my mind was trying to work out how these savage destinies could be circumvented and my son rescued for civilisation. I had no doubt that Lossio's words hid a plan to sacrifice my princess to their magic tree as they had sacrificed her mother; then what would happen to the babe, invested by them with a strange destiny? Snatched as a talisman by a rival tribe perhaps, or exposed to the gods on the heights of their mountain?

Gathering my wits, I spoke: "What use is there, then, in my staying? More for Rome I cannot do here. The solstice is approaching; the long days will light our journey south – if you will fulfill our contract and accompany me back to the borders of the empire."

Lossio hesitated, but soon agreed, I know not if through faithfulness to his bond, fear for his own safety among those people, or to collect his payment. He then himself proposed what I was going to ask: he would plead for me to be granted a final time alone with my wife and child.

Thus it was that I devised a plan to effect our deliverance from these fates. First I had to ascertain the mind of my princess, whether to come with me or not; then to be sure that, whatever her will, the babe would come with me. Lossio would have to find a girl to care for the infant, sufficiently disaffected from the tribe to wish to escape, strong and swift of foot to be no hindrance in our flight. If he could recruit one or two warriors similarly inclined, so much the better. Yet the hope still burned within me that my princess would desire to escape with us: was she not bound by love and duty to me, her husband and the father of her child? Why sacrifice herself to a savage god when she could live under the protection of the gods of Rome? Under what primitive delusion was she persuaded that her death here would work salvation for her tribe? Would it not be nobler to risk death fighting for her life – no worse fate would befall her but, with trust in a more glorious destiny, she might live on in honour and as a lady of Rome.

These sentiments I prepared to urge on her when our meeting was permitted. Two days later, all our preparations having been completed in secrecy, I was ushered into her presence. Her three guards with their huge swords were around the fire, and as I approached the couch where the princess lay, one, the tallest, followed close behind, another moved to the door to bar the exit. Did they suspect? I took the babe from the woman who was holding him and laid him in his mother's arms. Her eyes had been shut, but feeling the presence of her child she stirred, clasped him to her, opened her eyes and gazed at me. But what a hollow uncomprehending gaze, only faint flickers of love, hate or hope in its depths – some heavy herbs or will-destroying potion had taken her spirit. In despair I embraced her and whispered in her ear what I could of our plans and many exhortations to life and freedom. She uttered nothing, nor changed her gaze. I buried my face beside the child on her breast, scarce able to control my tears. Even had I wished to move away, my body could not respond, yet was seized by uncontrollable trembling. This agony lasted I know not how long when I felt the guard's hands on my shoulders, pressing me to rise. But this force upwards was resisted by the arms of my wife which now gripped onto me and could not be released. The guard, realising that he could not tear me away from her, and assuming that her drugged state would preclude her escape, instead moved to assist her up. And so with her volition or not, my princess, still clutching her babe, stumbled out between me and the guard to a farewell, or to freedom. The other guards followed, swords aloft; another escort appeared, bearing shields and spears. In such a procession we moved to the rampart gates where Lossio and his recruits waited in a crowd of onlookers.

We halted, me wishing to assess my opportunities now allies were present, the guards perhaps sensing a suitable place for farewell. The tall guard bent quite gently to the babe and lifted him, she this time offering no resistance. I took my son as if to give him a final embrace, but looked towards Lossio as a sign of readiness. Suddenly the princess, from standing as a statue of despair, head drooping, hair cascading down, came alive as if possessed. Her head lifted up, her face struck by a sudden shot of bright sunlight as dark clouds parted in the heavens, her hair streamed behind her as the wind rose. The people stood in wonder as she tore at the long hem of her robe, leaping out of its folds, clad only in a short tunic. Then even the strongest of the guards backed away as all of her limbs, seemingly independently, flailed around uncontrollably, only to coil up in preparation for a great leap forward and a race for freedom. As she dashed away, her guards stood motionless for an instant, but then called the lightly armed warriors to the pursuit. My party then took our chance to run, bearing the precious infant. At one point Lossio pulled me back, indicating a chance to escape in a different direction while the warriors hunted my wife, but I would have none of it. I knew she was running away to a new life with me, and somehow we would have to catch up with her, to get ahead, with enough distance between us and the main band to be able to fight off the vanguard, though how to accomplish this I had little idea.

By the time the chase had reached the great yew tree that was subject to such veneration, it looked as if in her frenzy she would well outpace her pursuers. But some signal must have gone ahead, for new warriors appeared from the heights in front and barred her way. She paused not, but tore on through their ranks, yet could not prevail against their numbers, and as we made up on her we saw her limbs being pinioned and herself dragged back towards the great tree. There I came to her, no one having tried to arrest me, and the girl came also who was carrying the infant, as his mother called first to have the child brought to her, but then her face changing, screamed to have him borne to safety. As the girl turned from her there appeared before the child the ancient hermit from across the river whom I had met so strangely on my first arrival. He stared at the child, then at the mother. He raised his withered arms to take the babe but my princess writhed her body as if in torment and shouted out in her tongue "Take me, take me!"

The old man motioned to the warriors who fell back from us to leave a passage eastwards for us to leave by. I turned back for a last desperate attempt to rescue my wife, but was prevented by the guards. Then Lossio and his friend pulled me away backwards, so that as I abandoned her I kept my eyes on her. Thus I saw what shall stay in my memory for ever. Under the direction of the hermit the warriors bound her wrists and ankles and tied her with her back to the massive trunk of the yew, the ropes on her wrists and ankles pulling her limbs out into a great letter X. As I was thus forced to forsake my loved one in saving my son, just before the horrid sight was obscured by distance and the crowd, I made out four men each bearing a great bronze nail which they began to hammer into place as if to fasten her hands and feet for ever to that cursed tree.

But I could not witness her final agony: the crowd between us massed together to block my view, and those alongside pushed me forward. As the press of the crowd built up behind me, those in front moved apart to form a path stretching ahead. Like some gigantic living processional way, it was continually extending as more barbarians – or those from behind running ahead – ever appeared in the forward distance, joining the parallels along which our course was forced.

In this way we progressed out of the guarded valley, but after we forded the stream in which I had first received my initiatory immersion, we were turned, not as I had intended towards the Tavus river, to retrace south-eastwards the way I had come, but northwards and upwards our little band was forced, up the wild gully that would lead finally to their holy mountain. Fear and horror gripped my heart anew as I understood that the sacrifice might not just be at the ancient yew, but on the mountain, and the victim my son. What of myself? Did these gods desire a foreign sacrifice? Or would alien blood pollute their sanctuary? The power of Rome could not protect me here. If I never returned would an expeditionary force come to seek me? Even if the imperial armies conquered this wild and distant land, would revenge for my death be part of their mandate? Would my disappearance even be noted by the authorities at home? By the time I am expected to return the legates will have changed, the tribunes demoted or transferred, who will bother to look up my file to wonder what happened to me? I have no influential family or friends to bring my loss to imperial notice – if I had I would not have been sent on this vain assignment to the ends of the earth.

As I trudged upwards through the trees and bushes lining the gully down which a ragged torrent fell, I meditated on my hopeless situation; and just as we reached the upper limit of the falls above a deep and gloomy pool, where the bushes began to clear and reveal an open sky and high, desolate moorland, I heard a commotion on one side. The wall of barbarians fell back as an apparently dense thicket seemed to shiver and a strange white shape glowed inside it. I stopped and stared and Lossio ran from my side towards this phenomenon, while our guards fell back in amazement. I seized the child from the nurse and pressed him to me, crouching down near the earth for protection and from weariness. My mind could no longer grapple with the future, or try to comprehend what significance this happening had, or what Lossio was doing – trying to save his life or mine I cared not. But as Lossio seized hold of the head of a miraculous pure white stag – for such it was, caught by its antlers in the thicket – another lesser white shape flitted over the greater, like a small but agile animal leaping over the stag's head, alighting on its back for an instant, then disappearing into the undergrowth. Then two of the young warriors leapt to Lossio's assistance, pinioning the stag's legs and pulling it free; but half of its antlers broke off to be left in the bush, so that the beast, shining like ivory or silver, seemed to have but a single gleaming horn on its forehead.[37]

At last, some hope and understanding crept upon me: could this beast, so pure and unique, be seen as a substitute for the sacrifice of my son? Such an apparition could well be a talisman, either as a noble white stag, or as the legendary one-horned beast. It must have been especially marked by the gods, the small animal alighting on its back could have been a hare and a sign from their moon goddess or for me from Diana herself. I lifted up the child on my right shoulder as if to present him to the holy beast that was to be his substitute, but some of the Caledonians had already bound the stag's feet and were cutting a long pole by which to carry it. They ignored me, lifting the pole with the beast suspended onto their shoulders, and setting off down the hill. Lossio made to follow them, I tried to stop him, but he pushed past, merely muttering in my ear what I thought to be base riddles and treachery: "Remember how Venus hid Aeneas," he said, then "West, west to the great garden of the sea."

My justifiable anger at being apparently abandoned and betrayed by my freedman somewhat mitigated my apprehension of danger to my son and myself, and I laboured upwards still holding the babe. My mind and heart were numb and obscure as if my spirit swirled around in a mist. In an effort to clear my brain, I lifted my head and looked upwards to where the peak of the mountain stood out in a blue sky. As if in sympathy with my state of mind, the air

[37] This scene may have been preserved in Caledonian and Pictish iconography – it bears a striking resemblance to an enigmatic carving on the St Andrews Sarcophogus (see cover illustration). The adoption of the unicorn by James IV as the Scottish heraldic bearer is, however, too far in the future to have any but the most tenuous connection.

round the summit seemed to condense and form into a white plume, almost like that which arises from the crater of our Vesuvius. This likeness brought me back to the strange words of Lossio – what could a Caledonian slave know of pious Aeneas, of whose exploits I had heard in my youth from the lips of the old poet himself?[38] Such deliberations I could not continue as the way up the mountain became steeper and more treacherous, with great rocks to be surmounted and giant boulders that had to be leapt onto or over. These obstacles did not hinder the natives, who, spurred on doubtless by the devils of the crags, would still push, pull and prod me no matter in what precarious position I found myself. Fearing for the safety of the babe, I relinquished him into the hands of the nurse, who, such is the agility of her race, was better able to leap from rock to rock. My concentration being on how to keep my footing and my balance, I did not notice how the mist had gathered and thickened until, as I was alighting on a particularly high and dangerous boulder, I saw the nurse and babe like apparitions above me in the mist, found myself scrabbling to my feet beside them and, gazing breathless round, saw no one else. As I steadied myself against the native girl, she herself looked round and must have understood the opportunity as quickly as I did, for together we crouched down, slid off the rock and made our secret way to where a sheltered rock, grown round with mountain plants, might hide us for a while from the savage horde.

As we lay together, the babe, the nurse, and I, we heard angry shouts – now near, now further off – from our guards. I hoped they were trying to find each other in the mist rather than co-ordinating a search for us. To comfort and warm my companions, and to keep us as insignificant as possible, I held them to me. I felt no shame at this intimacy with the barbarian girl – indeed it did, I think, imbue us both with confidence in the perilous journey we had to undertake.

After some time the mist thinned slightly and no more voices were heard. The girl – her name I ascertained was Brigda – was carrying some of our provisions, so I was able to refresh myself as she fed the infant. I still kept close lest the unusual activity or an infant cry might draw attention to us, and then we set off cautiously along the flank of the mountain. We were going west as Lossio had indicated, keeping to the south face as we descended, safely separated from the Caledonian camp by barren hills. The way sloped steeply with treacherous fields of loose stones precipitating many falls, but the girl bravely kept the babe safe, and, the air clearing as we rounded the end of the mountain, we saw a river and a lake stretching westward below us. Did these indicate the way to Lossio's great garden of the western sea?

[38] In Vergil's epic Venus sent a mist to allow Aeneas to approach Carthage in secrecy.

I questioned the girl, but could get little sense from her apart from her name, Brigda. Her own tongue was not even that of the Caledonians, but I repeated 'great garden'[39] accompanied by pointing to the west and miming the sea until she seemed to comprehend, and gestured, as I had surmised, to the distance where the lake met the horizon. She seemed somewhat unwilling to proceed in that direction, and as the light was fading with a dark cloud above us, we were both happy to stumble upon a spacious cave where we could conveniently shelter from the weather and from any pursuers. So rejuvenated was I by this night's rest that by morning I was able to reconcile my tormented mind to the last sight I had had of my princess: as I watched the girl feed the babe I was filled with a conjugal hope that somehow Lossio had effected her release. Now I could only console myself with the companionship of my son and his nurse as we made our way down to the water's edge and turned our faces westward. Our journey that morning was long but easy enough. We passed through great dark woods that hid us well until at last we came out to where the lake merged into a wet wilderness, a barren moor scarred with black pools and brown rivulets, stretching out before us, seeming without end.

The girl looked at the babe and me, shaking her head violently. I repeated 'sea garden, great garden' and she indicated again it was across this wilderness, but venture on it she would not. I took her in my arms to reassure her, and looking back over the lake spied a fleet of boats paddling towards us. I seized the child and, holding him in one arm, with the other I dragged the girl and ran furiously, bending low to avoid being seen, until we were both exhausted. Too tired to lift our feet, we fell over a clump of heather into a hollow in the moor. We both sustained minor injuries but managed to protect the child. This hollow we found to be well protected and quite dry. Here we might lie hidden from any pursuit. After lying there some time and having recovered our composure, I crawled up to the lip of the hollow to look out. I scanned the desolation for a sign of life – perhaps a line of searchers advancing over the moor; there was nothing.

Satisfied that our pursuers had lost us, I slipped down and jagged my knee on something sharp. I found half buried an ancient knife, its blade rust and mud encrusted and its hilt of curious workmanship. I surmised it had been lost here by some previous fugitive or dropped by a warrior waiting in ambush. We were certainly not the first to lie hidden in this hollow, nor perhaps would we be the last.

I resolved to keep the knife as a token that the gods were favouring our escape, and motioned to the girl to get ready to proceed. We would be safe, but uncomfortable, for a belt of driving rain had progressed from over the lake to

[39]   As we shall see, this refers to Lismore in the Firth of Lorne, but its pre-Gaelic name is thought to have been Tirafuir, 'the land of pasture'.

where we were. It soaked us as we clambered out but would serve well for concealment. But fear of capture was driven from my mind as hour after hour we dragged our weary bodies through marshes, heath and evil water below and around us. Nowhere was there to stop for rest or refreshment, no sign of where we were heading, grey rain all around. It was not until we were near to collapse from cold and fatigue and wet that Brigda pulled at my sleeve and pointed into the gloom ahead. Dimly I could just make out two dark shapes looming ahead on both sides of our route – two horrid mountains as it turned out, guarding the entrance to a dismal valley. As I approached I felt more and more as if we were entering the land of shades, and I gripped the talismanic dagger closely to reinforce the charm that must bring me through this fateful place. At least the ground was now firmer below our feet, but the wind howled along the defile through the stern, forbidding rocks.

Was it trust in the talisman or the girl's instinct gave me hope to carry on towards this devilish portal? I could scarce drag my own feet forward let alone give any help to the girl who was clutching the babe close against the elements. Yet the way ran downhill now, and the formless waters turned themselves into a swift stream. The rocks were dark above us and shrouded in mist, but the portion of sky in front seemed clearer. With some relief I saw that the girl was turning us away from that fearsome valley and instead took a narrow defile to the left, which at length opened out to reveal a fair stretch of blue water ahead.[40] As I was to discover, this was the head of an arm of the sea winding into the heart of the mountains, and when I sensed this furthest extremity of Ocean I rejoiced, even in my fatigue, in this distant link with Our Sea and even the land of Italy. Brigda too was possessed with a new power and ran on until, after a tiring age, we reached a mean hut on the shore. She flung aside the rags that covered its entrance and yelled a wild babble of sound to the interior. A woman appeared and embraced her, screaming also in a similar tone. At first I took this to be some weird barbarian ceremony, but then realised it was merely the joyous recognition of two people in another land with the same tongue. So it might be with me, if the gods permit, when in the not too distant future I meet another man with the real speech of Rome.

Glad as we were to have reached this habitation, there was little comfort here or help for our journey. These cottars had no boat but what would be better described as a floating basket quite unsuitable for our purpose – such a distant reach of the ocean admitted only the most primitive navigation. We were driven inside their hut as our heads were besieged by clouds of tiny biting flies that seem to be a plague inflicting this coast, feasting particularly on foreign flesh, so that it was better to suffer the smoke of the interior smarting

[40] The fugitives had crossed Rannoch Moor towards Glen Coe, turning south into Glen Etive.

our eyes than endure the myriad of pinpricks. After a painful rest and basic nourishment we continued our way at first light, picking our path among the rocks of the shore until about noon we came to a more open scene, the water stretching out to the west and the land more gentle and fertile. Some huts and small craft indicated active settlement, and we began to hope for some convenient transport. Soon we came upon a boat pulled up on the beach. Beside it two boys were idly throwing stones into the sea. The elder of these was fair and well featured, so skilled at spinning flat stones that he could project them a hundred paces skimming across the surface of the sea. The other boy, a few years his junior and lacking his form and grace, was endeavouring vainly but with strange persistence to emulate the elder. In reaction to our approach the elder looked wary and defensive; the look of frustration on the younger face gave way to a wide smile and shout of greeting, but his actual words were incomprehensible to me and, as it turned out, to my companion. She was, however, able to talk with the elder and negotiate for the use of the boat. We had little to offer, but the young boy saw my talismanic dagger and would have nothing else.

Terms being thus settled, the good-looking boy with great politeness urged us to embark as soon as possible; but this alarmed the youngster, who made wild signs of distress. I assumed that, in his simple way, although welcoming of strangers he had no desire to lose his boat, and I tried by gesture to reassure him, while his brother too tried forcibly to calm him. We were indeed pleased to proceed at once, as the tide – which so miraculously has a strong pull on these waters even among the mountains – had from its peak begun to run our way, and we now hoped to be able to reach the promised island by nightfall. So we left the shore and the boys, one staring solemnly after us, the other still gesticulating wildly; and we made good progress in fair weather: a pleasant journey in contrast to the hardships we had endured, the girl nursing my son and my thoughts on an imminent reunion with my princess, I imagined our dangers were behind us. The few inhabitants seemed not to be aggressive; there it seemed Scots and Caledonians lived together and the outreach of the ocean made them not unaccustomed to occasional visitors from the civilised world.

So our calm voyage continued until I began to make out what seemed to be the sound of distant waves. This lightened my heart as I thought it presaged the open sea, but as the roar grew louder I saw a less favourable omen. I know not how it was, but the younger of the two boys, the wild one, had somehow caught up with us and was running along the shore yelling frantically and waving uncontrollably. I stood up in the boat as the nurse clutched the babe, and I saw too late the reason for his consternation: ahead of us a line of white spume stretched from shore to shore as this arm of the sea in its entirety dropped in fury to the new level of the ocean several feet below.[41] A powerful current now seized the boat and drew it to its doom: as it plunged over the waterfall I was thrown out and fell first through the air and then down under the raging waves. I forced myself to the surface and searched for a sign of my son. But there was none. The boat indeed I could make out being carried away westward, keel upwards, and I thought I saw an arm clinging to it, so perhaps the nurse had survived, but nothing of my son. Then I saw him, emerging from the water, as if rising by himself from the waves. I shouted aloud with joy at this miracle, then saw that a pair of hands was grasping him, arms appeared, then the head of the wild boy, slowly but steadily moving towards the shore. Soon the child-bearer stood before me, the babe sitting aloft on his shoulder, the talismanic knife still firmly in his grasp, and I sank to my knees in thanksgiving to the gods.

Outlandish as the saviour of my child was, he did seem to know our purpose and the route we were set on. Communication with him was difficult or fruitless, but I trusted him to guide us to our destination. I followed as he loped over the rough ground still bearing the child. I did not know how long we would have to travel thus before the child would need his mother or a nurse, yet he seemed strangely contented, cast for the most part across the shoulders of the youth as a shepherd might carry a lamb. So we made good progress, partly along the twisting shoreline, partly across high ridges of land, until we came to a vantage position where the child-bearer halted and pointed across a channel of the sea to a long, low, green island, and on its shore a substantial fortified tower of stone, such as I had not expected to see in these barbarous regions.[42] I thought this was perhaps an outpost of some other emissaries from the civilised world, and this supposition was strengthened by the sight of a good sized vessel anchored nearby – not a Roman galley certainly, but maybe one of these wine traders from Gaul or Spain. I was soon to discover, however, that signs of civilisation do not always signify safety.

I proceeded quickly to the water's edge, gesturing as best I could to the mariners for aid; they could at least take us to the island – which I presumed to be the Great Sea Garden – if not to noble Rome herself. The child-bearer followed, reluctantly I thought, mouthing incomprehensibly and crying strangely at my back as he lagged further behind. I turned to urge him on, and found that two men had crept up behind me. They pinioned my arms and led me roughly to a small boat where I was seated and bound firmly. My captors then

---

41 The Falls of Lora, celebrated in Ossianic poems. At the narrowest part of Loch Etive at ebb tide the water "descends over the reef with the violence and noise of a lofty cataract" (Wardlock Guide to Oban).

42 Brochs such as the one still surviving on Lismore are now thought to date from this period.

set off after the child-bearer who had fled with the infant, but returned cursing – at least from the tone of their voices I assumed so, for though they seemed to speak a variety of the common tongue, it was a species unfamiliar to me. I proclaimed myself to them not just a Roman citizen but a Roman by descent and birth, a delegate of the Senate and the people of Rome, but this had no apparent effect, either from ignorance of true Latin or disbelief or malice. I was pushed to the bottom of the boat and brought on board the ship where I was left bound and with no sustenance in a noxious dark space below the decking.

I know not how long I spent in that foul stinking darkness; my only measure of time being my growing need for sustenance – not that I hoped for much from my captors. Nor could I find hope for the immediate future, my mind instead filled with the ironies of my capture by such outcasts of civilisation just as I had survived the ordeals of my long journeying and arduous mission among the barbarians. Yet, I found despair did not lead me to complete inaction. Indeed the discomfort of lying bound made me try any means to move, and eventually I found that the cords binding my wrists were not so firm as to prevent completely some action of my hands, albeit behind my back. Moreover the deprivation of the sense of sight only heightened my desire to ascertain the nature of my surroundings by what senses I had, and as I found more movement in my hands I felt more of the surface I was lying on with my fingers. By dint of what movement I could force out of my legs, I gradually explored more of the immediate space into which I had been flung. As I reached the further confines of my prison I discovered that this space also contained such maritime objects as one might expect to find below the deck. First my fingers made out a spar, or some sort of long shaft of wood, formed not unlike one of our *pilae* or javelins. I marked this in my mind as being perhaps of some use to me. Then some coils of rope, to the end of one of which was attached some metal object that might have been a kind of anchor. Feeling the edges of the metal to be quite rough, I began to work the cords about my wrists against them, until after long labour I hoped to free them.

But before this task had been completed I heard heavy treads above me. Fearing the discovery of my attempt to rid myself of my bonds, I rolled awkwardly away from the anchor just as a hatch above me was thrown open and a lamp appeared to descend – for such was the stygian gloom of that place that the light illuminated nothing of my surroundings, dazzling my eyes as it was brought up to my face. I could make out nothing of its bearer, who seized my head and muttered something incomprehensible, then forced a flask of evil water to my lips, and thrust a stale crust of bread into my mouth before the light disappeared into the night above. Such was my captors' gesture at preventing my starvation, and indeed I welcomed it as a sign that they wished me alive; while if they had presented my with proper food and drink they would have had to have loosed my hands to eat and drink and would have discovered my attempt to sever the cords. As it was, now I could recommence my task, and begin the painful inch by inch journey to position my back against the anchor. Ages it took, for my hands to be free so I could begin to liberate my feet from their bonds. My eyes perceived daybreak by a sliver of light through the hatch above me, just as I had freed myself to reach out towards where I thought there must be a ladder that would lead to the hatch and the open deck.

I had been praying to Mercury to aid my deliverance; my supplications might have been better addressed to Neptune. The sickening rolling of the ship at anchor had seemed to me a mere adjunct to the vile condition in which I had been held, and I had been so preoccupied with freeing myself that I had not noticed any increase in its motion. I know not what disagreement between the gods had come to a head, but just as I had been graced with deliverance from my bonds and stretched up towards the light, a sudden agitation of the vessel threw me down again onto the filthy deck. As I attempted to regain my balance, the motion becoming ever more violent, I heard yells from above, the pounding of feet and when these noises subsided, the drumming of rain on the deck. One favour the gods allowed me – the crack in the hatch which had shown me the light and through which now water began to drip was forced wide by the elements and I could see my way, though what use I could make of this opportunity I knew not. I found the spar which I had thought to be like a javelin and which now I thought might be of use and tentatively and precariously attempted the ascent to the hatch. When at length I could peer out with my head just at a level with the deck I could see through the deluge men urgently engaged in whatever would save the ship from such a violent storm as had suddenly descended upon it, wrenching it from its anchorage and blowing it towards the shore. The men being occupied and the lashing rain obscuring my actions, I crept out of the hatch and across the deck, sliding the last few paces in the wet as the ship pitched over, and then gripping the weatherboards at the edge of the hull. I peered over the side and saw the shore perilously close beyond the breakers, and in the wild sea, to my amazement a small boat almost overwhelmed and in it figures that seemed in my fevered imagination to be none other than my son's nurse whom I had lost to the seas before and two men like to my princess's former guards. I knew not if these were real or shades on the journey to the underworld – to which interpretation the infernal nature of the tempest conferred great credence – but further consideration was interrupted by a fierce yell behind me. I turned and saw one of my captors charging at me with a knife in his hand. I rose up despite the agitation of the ship, raised the spar high in my right hand, and discharged it towards my foe as I committed myself to Ocean and leapt into the waves.

THE STORY ACCORDING TO LOSSIO, FROM THE THIRD LETTER

I had left the Roman on a high ridge of the sacred mountain. It seemed that the gods, who were driving that family to some dreadful fate, had relented: I saw two hopeful signs. First, the plume of mist swirling from the mountain peak might just descend and expand into sufficient cover for an agile fugitive to elude his pursuers on the rough terrain of the heights; second, we came across a young white stag caught by its antlers in a thicket: this itself would signify to the superstitious that the gods were suggesting a sufficient substitute for the sacrifice, yet it was further marked by the sight of a hare startled by our approach seeming to leap over the stag. Then the beast's antlers snapped as it freed itself, leaving it with but a remnant which the credulous could take to be the single horn carried by their legendary holy beast. I had quickly to work out how to benefit both the child and the mother from these occurrences: the Roman and the nursemaid would have to take their chance in the mist, the white stag would have to go to save the mother. Amazed by the sight, the war band gladly obeyed my instructions to bind the beast and carry it down to the sacred tree.

I was not mistaken in my assessment of the priest. As a seer and mystic he believed in the sacrifice, and as the guardian of the traditions of the nation, he had to see it carried out. Yet his long experience had given him a pragmatic sensitivity, and he seized on the chance to free the human victim. He greeted the warriors with the unicorn ceremoniously, calling on the queens to award them great honours. Standing between the beast and the still cruciform princess he uttered a long impromptu incantation; then led the warriors with their new victim round to the opposite side of the tree where the ancient trunk had formed a great curve round a hollow. Into this space the beast was forced, but how it was dispatched I did not see, as I was now permitted to go to the princess and unbind her hands and feet from the bronze nails to which they were fastened. As her first hand was freed she attempted to struggle against me, and I had to whisper to her the prospect of her freedom and reunion with her child. Once released she collapsed upon me, but I urged her to gather her strength and slip away with me while we had the chance.

Thus it was that I was able to convey Pontius' wife out of the stronghold, the elders of the Caledonians being occupied by the mysteries of the sacred tree and their holy mountain. I had saved one victim and hoped that the Roman could take his chance to save the other. Any doubts I had I could not reveal to my companion, as we stumbled in haste along the steep valley westward. The sacrificial ceremonies had drained the people from this region, so we met no one, but I still feared that some faction might pursue us, especially if the Roman had indeed escaped with the child. I put my faith in the nurse to guide him: a girl of the Scots of the west, she had been captured by the Caledonians in a tribal war and raised as a domestic slave. She would relish her own freedom and the chance to return to her lands. She and the Roman had prepared for a journey, and even he could make fair speed; the princess, however, was exhausted by the traumas she had experienced, and suffered from lack of food and the effects of the drugs that had been forced upon her. She was clad only in the flimsy remnants of the robe she had torn herself out of, and I had to share with her my cloak as well as the few provisions I had carried with me. In our land the summer days are long in light, but sometimes cold and damp; the ways through the hills are rough and stony or wet and marshy. A hard time we had, struggling over a rain-desert which provided nothing to eat but the tiny fruits of the mountains, but at last we came down to the lower woodlands and then to those narrow arms of the ocean that characterise this part of Britain, winding as they do into the hills themselves. Here live sea people, like the slave girl originally from Hibernia, who could safely provide sustenance and transport for us.

A Roman coin I carried purchased us food, raiment, and a boat to take us to that island which I hoped the others would find. Called Great Garden in both Caledonian and Scottish tongues, it is a long and fertile isle lying in the midst of a great channel that is part of a system of valleys, lakes and rivers that splits Caledonia in half, and but a day's journey by boat from where we had come down to the salt water. As we sailed down the channel, the sky cleared and the sun warmed us; the water turned as azure as the sky, and the green of the hillsides and the islets brought to mind the Eden the Jews claim to be heir to. Does your Christ also promise a return to that blessed land? No place of peace and plenty can distance itself from strife: our idyllic voyage brought us to where a great tower had been built on an eminence near the shore. Not a structure to compare with the giant fortifications of Italy, Greece or Egypt, certainly, but remarkable in this far off place: for where the sciences of civilisation are slow to reach, so are the sciences of war. Our tribal conflicts may be barbarous and petty, but they cause infinitely less suffering than the might of Alexander or Caesar. Our warrior chiefs are generally content with a ditch and palisade round a hilltop or headland, but better defences are needed against the raiders seeking their stock of workers to sell in the markets of Rome. When the galleys of the strangers are sighted the people shut themselves up in the tower, until the raiders go off to look for easier prey. If only there had been such a tower near my home, my life would have been very different! So effective a defence are these towers that I have heard that every chief of the northern shores is building one, against the Scythian pirates who are bent on satisfying the greed of Rome.

However, our refuge was not to be so easily entered. A longship of southern type was anchored in the roads and we had to approach warily. Slavers might be watching the tower for any stragglers, or even hoping to bargain with the besieged, I hoped that Pontius and the child were already inside, or else would have the sense to keep clear of the intruders. We moved carefully among the bushes along the shoreline until we came to a small cave hidden by undergrowth which would provide good shelter and concealment. The princess, however, broke away from me and ran to the water. It was indeed a strange sight she was gazing at. A wild looking youth seemed to be sitting unsupported in the sea and paddling himself towards us. Even stranger, he had in his lap a babe, which the princess had no doubts in recognising as her own. It was a miracle enough, because the coracle in which the lad was sailing was so flimsy that it was invisible in the waves, and he had an uncanny sense of where to find the babe's mother. We hurried into the cave where the youth tried to tell us what had happened. He had been cursed with a strange tongue of his own, but he persevered in repeating his words in different forms until we got the main part of his message: that he had rescued the babe from the sea but the foreign man had been taken by the slavers.

We sat and discussed what we should do. Neither of us would have risked our lives for the Roman – nothing in his character deserved such a sacrifice. Yet the princess must have felt some kind of passion for the father of her child, while I was in a quandary. Roman faith would have been for a freedman to his master: but that was the faith according to the masters. My own faith was for my own people and for the innocents, my duty to save a princess of my country and her infant. I had been bought by Pontius like an animal at a market, and a taste of slavery for him would be just recompense. Would it dispel his vanity and strengthen his character? Yet he had put a simple trust in me, and besides he had treated me reasonably well, unlike the slavers who had first captured me. It was the slavers who deserved retribution, even if it was only to deprive them of their captive. What were they going to do with him anyway? He was not such a specimen to get a good price in an open mart – more likely they knew he was a Roman and were hoping for a ransom. A dangerous business for a common slaver, more likely to end in execution than profit. I left the princess to feed her babe and crept out to the bushes from where I could see the longship and keep a watch for any activity.

The scene held a peace that concealed its dangers. The ship bore no sign of its treacherous purpose, the great stone tower concealed the terror and discomfort of the hundreds of people that must be gathered inside. What could we do? We could not storm the ship and release the captive, neither could we easily enter the tower. Even if we reached it in safety, they would not open the gate to strangers when the slavers were around. I watched until evening and saw nothing move, but as the light faded a small boat could be seen in the south. It approached the ship slowly and I could just make out in it two men and a girl. Suddenly the silence was shattered by our strange young friend who must have been crouched behind me and had leapt up yelling and rushing madly along the shore in the direction of the boat. He had recognised the girl as the child's nursemaid. He had been unable to save her before, so some instinct drove him to her rescue now.

I started to follow the youth, hoping to restrain him lest his exuberance attracted the attention of the slavers, but stopped. I could not prevent him from wading wildly into the sea to meet the boat and bring its occupants to our refuge, but I was afraid that it was not to save us from the slavers that these young men had journeyed so far. More likely they hoped to find and seize the princess and her infant and take them back to their people. They would not help release the Roman from his captivity, but rather claim him as their property and demand from the slavers their share of his value. Yet I had a suspicion that these Caledonians had come seeking the princess out of something other than duty or anger – they had been her companions of old and the guards of her confinement, and I wondered if she could manage to bend them to her feminine will.

I remained concealed to see how they would react to the wild youth's greeting. They had no patience with his uncouth tongue: he was not of their people and they doubtless dismissed him as a simpleton. His eagerness to embrace the girl whom he thought he had lost alarmed them; they pulled him away roughly, and when he persisted shouted at him coarsely and struck him till he fell on his knees in the shallows. They ignored him then, addressing themselves to beaching their boat and making camp for the night. Seeing them preoccupied, I cautiously emerged and gestured to the youth to follow me to the cave, where I told the princess what I had seen. She darted to the mouth of the cave and I had to hold her back, warning her that she and the babe were in danger of being taken. She gave the child to the youth to hold and stayed with me where she could watch the newcomers; yet nothing she said showed any concern for Brigda – who might well have relieved the youth of his unmanly duty – only scarcely controllable impulses to rejoin her old companions, regardless of the consequences.

The evening had been warm and still – luckily we had not kept the fire up in the cave so there was no smoke to betray our refuge – and this unaccustomed weather held until morning, when the young warriors began to relaunch their boat, forcing Brigda into it. The early sky, however, did not clear, but darkened as if the day had concluded before it had properly begun. Heavy drops of rain foretold the coming of a squall, which caught the boat and threw it down the straits towards the slave ship. Soon the driving rain obscured my view, but I could just make out the ship wallowing in the now heavy sea and being borne before the wind towards the shore.

I ran back to the cave and called for the youth to come with me and for the princess to stay inside, safe with the child; yet as the youth and I battled through the wind and rain along the shore, turning our heads to get the weather from our eyes, I saw her stumbling after us with the babe bound to her breast. I had no clear idea of why I was trying to reach what might be a scene of disaster – an instinctive desire to witness a wreck, or an unformed plan to rescue the Roman and the nurse. I could understand even less what drove the princess to expose her baby, who had suffered much already, to such a storm. At last we reached the beach beside the great tower, from whose walls a crowd was now watching the drama: the ship had sheered off from the rocks and had disappeared south behind a screen of rain, but the small boat had been blown onto the breakers which had overturned it, spilling its contents onto the wave pounded shingle – the two Caledonians, the nurse, and the apparently lifeless body of the Roman.

There was no time to find out what had happened. The gate of the tower opened and a crowd rushed out as the youth and I ran to the Roman to see if there was any help we could give him. He was cold but perhaps his spirit was still within him; as we pulled him out of the water I looked to see if the princess had come, and saw her, running not to the father of her child, but to throw herself on the body of the fairest of the young warriors, keening and wailing, and holding the babe aloft as if supplicating the fury of the heavens. Indeed the gods seem random in their apportioning of fate. Ocean had delivered the weak and pampered Roman up to us alive, while Vipo, the strongest of our young warriors, had been killed as he was thrown from the boat, a sharp rock splitting his skull.

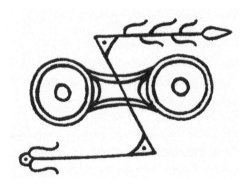

FURTHER EXTRACTS FROM
THE THIRD REPORT OF M. PONTIUS

I cannot give an exact report of what transpired after my leap from the ship. I endured a mighty battle with the waves and must have reached my saviour's boat, for I have a recollection of being pulled from the sea and given some welcome attention by Brigda. Yet the motion of the flimsy craft above the waves was almost as objectionable as being under them, and I could not observe what if any progress it was making; but of a sudden I was cast once again into the turbulent sea and know not what happened thereafter, until I found myself being hauled roughly up a beach and left half dead on stony ground. After an age alone in agony, I was seized by two strangers and borne inside a stone edifice of coarse yet massive construction, and abandoned again in the damp and gloom. When I was sufficiently recovered to take stock of what I feared to be further imprisonment, I realised that, weak as I was, I was free to move. I had made some initial exploration of my situation when I saw several figures approaching and thought it prudent to resume a recumbent position; I felt much relief at the familiarity of the voices that approached me. I opened my eyes cautiously and recognised not only the nurse Brigda and Lathmon, the young Caledonian from the lake palace, but behind them my own princess and my son. Elated, I endeavoured to rise, but discovered myself too weak. However, the princess approached with the babe and gave due salutation, while the nurse fetched some coarse but dry raiment, examined my body for major injury, and administered a reviving potion. Then Lossio appeared and recounted the events I was unaware of: that the structure that sheltered us – the same tower I had seen before my capture – was a defence the natives had built for protection against the slave traders who had been terrorising the coasts; that he and the princess had reached here to be met by the wild youth and the babe; that two Caledonians in pursuit had found the nurse on the shore before being engulfed by the storm, only just accomplishing my rescue before all of us were cast up on the shore near the tower; and that there the other of the Caledonians, Vipo by name, had lost his life.

The death of her compatriot seemed to affect the princess adversely and eclipsed what joy she felt at the safe reunion with her husband. She kept her distance, clutching the child always to her, and left the discussion of our plans to myself in consultation with Lossio and Lathmon. The latter Caledonian apparently was prepared to help us contrive a safe journey to civilisation, the desire to inflict vengeance on the slaver being stronger than any duty to return us to his own people. For myself I felt my duty was to punish those who had inflicted imprisonment on a Roman citizen, notwithstanding any right they had to carry on their despicable trade, necessary though it might be to the economy of the empire. Moreover, to take possession of their ship seemed to be the obvious way to effect our passage to civilisation.

The report was that the ship had been driven for some miles before, through fate or skilful seamanship, going aground relatively intact. Some of the captives still aboard were rumoured to have freed themselves during the storm: one of them was said to have played a part in the safe beaching of the ship. More news came with the wild youth, who, despite his uncouth tongue, could divine good intelligence and Brigda had some ability to decipher his gabble: while some of the escaped captives who belonged to neighbouring tribes were making their way home, others were seamen who had been seized in acts of piracy and would certainly be willing to take over the ship and sail it home. They were of the Dumnonii of the south west of Britain, which region would be a good staging post for a journey back to Our Sea. To them, then, with the wild youth as a guide, Lossio went to negotiate an alliance.

The simple hospitality of the island allowed me, while waiting for the results of the negotiation, to recover from the trials I had undergone since my departure from the capital of the Caledonians. Lathman and the island chiefs were more concerned with arranging a suitable funeral for his companion than planning an attack on our enemies. The princess, my wife, had fallen into a lethargy; she left to Brigda the task of tending to my needs, absorbed herself only in the care of Lucius, our son. This I could partly understand, after what she, too, had experienced and the long separation from her infant. Yet I could not help but feel it unbecoming for the wife of a Roman to take on the work of a nursemaid – even among these barbarians it is the custom for the children of their 'nobility' to be given to a respectable woman to be raised. The death of her compatriot, Vipo (a childhood playfellow), must have affected her, but I would have expected this to be compensated for by the prospect of a successful outcome of our adventure. Yet she took the child from the shelter of the tower in the chill of the early dawn to follow the island men to the place where the burial was being prepared, at the top of the low ridge that ran down the centre of this long narrow island.[43] There they built a box of stone slabs, and at noon after lengthy and strange ceremonies, Lathmon brought the body of his friend to be laid therein. A mound of stones was piled up over the grave, then a covering of soil, and finally a pyre of wood which was set alight as if to prolong the light for the dead warrior's journey to the other world. The fire was kept burning throughout the short night; the mourners left at sunrise; my wife could not be prevailed upon to accompany them, but remained sitting by the tomb, holding our child, until Lossio and the wild boy successfully returned. Nor would she have abandoned the remains of the hero,

---

[43]   This may have been at Cnoc Aingeil, 'the fire hill', where there is a cairn associated with the burial of the dead in ancient times.

had not the youth ritually deposited the talismanic dagger in the ashes, and then Lossio and Lathmon managed to persuade her to give Lucius into the care of Brigda and come to take her part in the planned capture of the ship. *(Third Report sealed on the eve of battle).*

THE STORY ACCORDING TO LOSSIO: MORE FROM THE THIRD LETTER

What was I planning for myself? Why not leave the Roman to find his own way home? I could have made my way to my own people, to the seas of the north which I had not seen since I was a boy. Yet I found myself setting out to organise the capture of a pirate ship to transport a feckless Roman, and presumably his wildcat Caledonian wife and luckless child, back to the empire that had sent him on a foolish mission. Was I destined to rejoin his world, from which fate seemed to have offered me an escape? Or did a higher destiny ordain that I had to safeguard the child Lucius Pontius – so that he could live to be the executioner of your God? And I left to make a life among the whirlpools and eddies of a ramshackle empire.

Anyway, there was little difficulty, once I had located the seamen who had escaped from the slave ship, in enlisting their support in our plan to take it over. Indeed they had formed such a scheme themselves, and only needed some persuasion to allow the Roman to join us. When they realised that he was the one who had killed the chief slaver with a fateful lunge of a broken spar, they applauded and laughing adopted the 'spear thrower' as one of their own. One of them with some knowledge of the Latin tongue, called out *"Pilate, pilate, salvator nostre"*, giving the Roman the nickname of 'spearman', which through his vanity that was oblivious to the mockery inherent in its bestowal, he adopted as his family surname, Pilate.[44]

There was more uncertainty on my return to the tower, as the princess was still mourning the death of Vipo with an intensity that only the most naive of husbands could accept without jealous suspicions. She came along with us out of hopeless resignation, only her burning will to live – having avoided the sacrificial death that was to have been her fate – kept her from following the friend of her heart into the underworld. We had assembled a sizable army from the islanders who had lived for long with the fear of slavery, so that added to the skill of our seamen allies and the mythical reputation of our 'spearman', we had a force so formidable that the remnants of the pirates, with little hope of victory or of freeing their ship for escape, surrendered after a brief skirmish and suffered that slavery which they had imposed on many others.

[44] According to Anne Wroe, Pilate's surname (or more properly his cognomen) may have commemorated a feat of spear throwing.

So I embarked on a new voyage as a free man but with no idea of my destination.[45] With me travelled the Roman and his wife and her child, whose guardian I still seemed to be. The child's nurse, Brigda, displaced in her duties to the child by the mother, and seeing her new life to be there on the islands, wished to stay behind despite a rather unseemly entreaty by Pontius, who had become dependent on her feminine comforts. Lathmon would return to his people, whose freedom he had vowed to defend. He had seen enough of the world now to know what he had to fight against. But that world was the world I would live my life in. One last ferlie I cannot explain: just as we were sailing Brigda came running to the shore and leapt aboard, I cannot say to join us, for she kept herself apart. It was as if some force that we knew not of was pulling her to a new world.[46]

FROM THE FINAL REPORT OF M. PONTIUS NOW SURNAMED PILATUS

About this battle I can report that the gods granted us a notable victory, for which I performed due sacrifice. A good number of the natives wished to follow my leadership, together with the mariners we freed from captivity, as, accompanied by the Caledonian warriors and the princess, I led the attack on the pirates. We marched in good order to surround the ship. Once in position, my followers bestowed upon me a great throwing spear as our standard, and raised the cry "Pilatus, Pilatus!" in reference to my success in killing the pirate leader with the missile which I now believed the gods had put into my hands. These shouts and their implication struck terror into those of the pirates who still had any desire to resist – for many had already fled – and they were either cut down in flight by my followers, or surrendered themselves into the same bondage into which they had so often bound others. Such was their Fortune, while myself and my companions, whom they had in vain attempted to enslave, now had command of their ship, and to the acclamations of those remaining on the shore, set sail for the south and for civilisation.

Our course lay down the narrow gulf in which the island was situated, and then through a strait between a good sized island, Malaios by name,[47] and the mainland. Here the ocean opened out somewhat, yet we were it seemed surrounded still by islands, some near, some far. We were now more exposed

---

[45] Lossio, or his descendants may have eventually returned to Britain: a Roman inscription at Colchester translates as "grandson of Lossio the Caledonian".

[46] In Gaelic folklore St Brigit was borne by angels to the Holy Land to be the Virgin Mary's midwife – a favourite theme of Arts and Crafts artists.

[47] Mull: this is the form of the name in Ptolemy.

to the elements raging in the Western Ocean, and a strong west wind hampered our way southwards, blowing us towards a large isle to the east which was marked by two peaks rising up into the clouds.[48] As we were driven nearer, I espied an opening to the north east of the island which might lead us to shelter if there was clear water to the lea of the land. I gave the command to steer for it, but the mariners were loath, fearing, I assumed, danger from shoals and reefs. Then we saw a small boat coming from that very place, and at a good speed, faster than one would think their oars could drive. This seemed a good omen, and I urged the mariners on, though I admit events showed my interpretation to be incorrect. Indeed, both Lossio and my wife came to urge a different course, although I could not understand what they feared – so obscure are the superstitions these people have. But as we came to the point of the long island and turned into the strait between it and its neighbour, what appeared was far more terrible than anything they might have feared. For a great pit appeared before us in the ocean and the ship was borne before it by the terrible force of a fierce Charybdis.[49] While many on board were seized by panic, some even calling for the child to be thrown into this pit to appease the spirits of the deep, I called on the master to keep his nerve and steer past the chasm, the wind behind us being of sufficient force to carry us through. So he did, as the princess took the babe and held him aloft at the prow, as if indeed to present him as an offering to the gods of the Ocean for our salvation, but in truth to save him from the hands of the superstitious, while challenging the force of Fortune and the sea. Thus it was that my prayers were heard, the mariners' skill was sufficient, the wind maintained its primacy over the power of the water: our momentum took us past the horrid pit, and looking back we saw it closing up as if in frustration. We gained the open water to the east of the isle, and found a sheltered haven to recover from the ordeal.

I cannot well describe the quietude we now experienced, having triumphed over our enemies and the powers of nature. Sailing along the sheltered shore of this long island, we found the seas to be as calm as our souls. The land did indeed seem rough and little cultivated, the abode of wild beasts more than men; from the smooth waters we spied bear, deer in great numbers and when we beached the ship to attend to its hull we set fires round it at night to keep off wolves. Yet we felt no fear, the sand shelved gently, the land curved round us as if in protection, and we slept on the soft turf as if it was the finest couch.

Then, the tip of the long island having been reached, we found a broader, fairer isle well peopled. We passed beneath some higher ground where rough cliffs gave only occasional shelter – though where we did stop we found the

---

[48] Jura?

[49] The notorious whirlpool of Corrievracken obstructs the strait between Jura and Scarba.

water in the tumbling streams to be of the purest but dark tasting;[50] then we came to fertile ground where we anchored in a fair haven and bartered provisions from the natives. Here the night was so calm, we sat and listened to the quiet, as if possessed by the spirit of the place, and seemed to hear a singing in the silence, the Nymphs and Naiads of the sea and shore in concert.[51]

We might well have stayed at this enchanted isle, for as we rounded its extremity, the wind from the ocean, so long denied its power upon us, set upon us in fury. The next days – I cannot say how many – were worse that any I have known, as the master battled to reach the north-east coast of Hibernia, which land afforded some defence against the wind and waves. The passage between that island and the west of Britain has been previously reported, so I need not detail it, nor the misery we endured until at last we gained the south-west tip of Britain. To safely clear the fearsome cliffs and rocks of this extremest corner of the land, our master bore out to sea and found a haven in the deep, a cluster of islets difficult to access in ignorance,[52] but the crew being from these parts brought us to safety where the water was still and clear and we could rest again. From there a short but stormy passage took us back to a wide bay on the British shore where sits the tall mount called Ictis that is an island or not depending on the tides,[53] a port long known to mariners from Our Sea for trade in the tin in which Dumnonia[54] is rich. This being the destination of our friends who had brought us thus far, we said farewell and set ourselves to find a ship to bear us home.

The final pages of this manuscript, as so often happens, are dirty and torn, but it appears that Pilate and his companions were able to find passage on a ship going to Spain. Landing at the mouth of the Ebro, they journeyed up river to Seville, where they stayed for some time, sending reports to Rome of their safe arrival. Pilate himself, if not the others, may have crossed the Sierra to the coast and taken ship for Rome. Where and when he submitted his final report is not clear, but the following shows how it was received:

---

[50] As the distillers of Islay malts know to this day.
[51] Perhaps the singing sands near Port Ellen.
[52] Scilly?
[53] St Michael's Mount.
[54] Cornwall.

ASSESSMENT

These scrolls were submitted by M. Pontius (allegedly surnamed Pilatus) on the day before the kalends of September AUC 751 purporting to be the executive summary of his quarterly project reports covering the field action years of the Northern Britain (Caledonian) information project AUC 748–750, compiled in accordance with para II subsection XXXV(a) and submitted at the end of the project as allowed for under exception IIIB of subsection XXXV(c).

At first glance these documents might well be cast into the furnace without further perusal. M. Pontius commences with the kind of formality typical of officers with no reporting experience, conveying little or no useful information. He later abandons this style in favour of a personal and doubtless fanciful history more suited to some so-called epic written by a popular poetaster than the imperial information service. Among all the supposed adventures he enlarges on, there are very few facts, and hardly any of these are useful for our diplomatic or military purposes. There is therefore no point in passing them on to a higher authority, but I recommend allocating them for storage rather than destruction, only on two grounds: (i) they might conceivably be useful to trainers as examples of how *not* to write reports and (ii) if any interest is revived at some future date in contacts with these North British barbarians, this might serve, not so much as a source of information, but as a warning of the dangers of deviating from Roman convention and the direction of the SPQR, and of the importance of maintaining an impersonal and impartial stance at all times.

They should be marked: "Reserved – for approved eyes only"

As for the claim for salary and expenses from M. Pontius, in view of the unsatisfactory nature of his expedition and report, I recommend that only his basic allowance be paid. Despite his claims to the contrary, it can be assumed that he returned with sufficient booty to compensate him for his service, such as it was. There is no need to consider him for another post, but he should be kept under surveillance in case any covert sympathy for the barbarians should remain. The same obviously applies to his so-called wife and the freedman Lossio the Caledonian. The barbarian woman, Brigda, has not yet been traced, but this should be the highest priority. As for the child, his education should be carefully supervised, as given the circumstances of his birth and if properly trained, he might be made use of in some way by the government in whatever future circumstances the gods might decree for the glory of our republic and Empire.

C. Popolus, prefect.

BIBLIOGRAPHY

For what is known about the real and legendary Pontius Pilate, Anne Wroe's book is fascinating. Evidence for the Caledonians is sparse and unreliable – Agricola's account of the Roman campaign against them is half a century later than our time and may be more imaginary than factual.

I have assumed that the first Picts were largely later Caledonians under another name, although this may disputed. In any case not much more is known reliably about the Picts – even their famous symbols are a mystery. But folk tradition and place-names may point to some ideas that an imaginative recreation can build on. Among the books I have consulted or referred to are:

Breeze, D. J., *Roman Scotland* (London, 1996)

Breeze, D. J., Thoms, L. M. and Hall, D. W. (eds), *First Contact – Rome and Northern Britain* (Tayside and Fife Archaeological Committee, Perth, 2009)

Campbell, Duncan, *The Book of Garth and Fortingall* (Inverness, 1888)

Davies, Norman, *The Isles, A History* (London, 1999)

Dixon, Nick, *The Crannogs of Perthshire: A Guide* (Perth, 2009)

Henderson, Isabel, *The Picts* (London, 1967)

Holinshed, Raphael, *Historie of Scotland* (London, 1587)

Macara, Duncan, 'The Parish of Fortingall' in the *1st Statistical Account of Scotland* (Edinburgh, 1791)

Mackintosh-Smith, Tim (ed.), *The Travels of Ibn Batuta* (London, 2002)

Mackenzie-Dodds, Ruary, *Aberfeldy: A History of a Highland Community* (Aberfeldy, 2010)

Maxwell, G. S., *The Romans in Scotland* (Edinburgh, 1989)

Perth and Kinross Heritage Trust, *Fortingall, Kirk and Village* (Perth, 2006)

Ritchie, Walter, *The Isle of Lismore* (Lismore, 2005)

Sharpe, Richard (trans.), *Adamnan of Iona: Life of Columbus* (Harmondsworth, 1995)

Sherley-Price, Leo (trans.), *Bede: A History of the English Church and People* (Harmondsworth, 1955)

Sjoestedt, Marie Louise, *Gods and Heroes of the Celts* (London, 1949)

Skene, W. (ed.), *Johannes de Fordoun, Chronicle of the Scottish Nation* (Edinburgh, 1872)

Smythe, Alfred P., *Warlords and Holy Men* (London, 1984)

Stewart, Alexander, *A Highland Parish* (Glasgow, 1928)

Strachan, David, *The Carpow Logboat* (Perth, 2010)

Tacitus, Cornelius, *Agricola* (Harmondsworth, 1970)

Thomson, Derick S. (ed.), *The Companion to Gaelic Scotland* (Glasgow, 1994)

Watson, W. J., *The Celtic Placenames of Scotland* (Edinburgh, 1926 & 1993)

Wheater, Hilary, *Aberfeldy to Glenlyon & Kenmore and Loch Tay* (A Guide in Hand, Aberfeldy, 1982)

Wroe, Anne, *Pontius Pilate* (London, 1999).